PUSHED
A COLLECTION OF SHORT PLAYS
ABOUT PEER PRESSURE

by Nicole B. Adkins, Jeff Goode, Adam Hahn, Samantha Macher, Greg Machlin, Wendy-Marie Martin, Liz Shannon Miller, Jonathan Price, Mike Rothschild and Dave Ulrich

www.youthplays.com
info@youthplays.com
424-703-5315

TABLE OF CONTENTS

PRODUCTION NOTES

Pushed is a collection of short plays exploring peer pressure and its intersection with other real issues that teens face.

The plays can be performed as individual pieces or grouped together in any combination to create a show of the desired length and performed under the title *Pushed*.

PRODUCTION HISTORY

Pushed was conceived and developed by Nicole B. Adkins and Jeff Goode in collaboration with SkyPilot Theatre Company in Los Angeles under founding artistic director Bob Rusch and written by members of the company's Playwrights Wing.

It was first workshopped at Determined to Succeed, an educational non-profit organization in Los Angeles on September 21, 2013, directed by Jeff Goode, with the following cast:

Nicole B. Adkins, Zelika Chante, Jude Evans, Arden Haywood, Jason Kobielus, Morgan Lariah, Franci Montgomery, Niki Nowak and Ethan Zachery Scott.

Special thanks to Determined to Succeed Program Director / High School Coordinator Angel Honda, Executive Director Abby Adams, and student responders Brittany Aguilar, Krystal Briseno, Katherine Calderon, Sara Elmourabit, Raul Gonzalez, Gabriela Hernandez, Chris Madrigal, Diana Ovalle, Diana Pena, Mario Santos, Jackie Trejo, Isaiah Tulanda, Josh Tulanda.

Pushed was further developed through a staged reading on June 7, 2014 at The Young Actor's Studio under the direction of Jeff Alan-Lee & Andrew Shafer, with the following cast:

Guts (aka *Once upon a Time in the Peanut Gallery*) by Dave Ulrich
ZOE - Emily Kilroy
DERRICK - Josh Drummond
BUTT CHIN - Henry Kamp
RATATOUILLE - Johnathon Kidd Pollock

Six of Beer by Adam Hahn
BRICE - Josh Drummond
MARK - Alejandro Cervin
NARRATOR - Amanda Horowitz

B-E Aggressive by Samantha Macher
JANAE - Emily Kilroy
ANA - Noelle Backman
OLIVIA - Sareh Wilburn
CRYSTAL - Hannah Guterman
DELANEY - Sharon Rodas

Foam by Mike Rothschild
MADISON - Noelle Backman
HUNTER - Amanda Horowitz
CHRIS - Selina Alvarez
HARVEY - Sharon Rodas

Out Post by Nicole B. Adkins
CRUZ - Shir Zahavi
ISABELLA - Miya Parry

Awareness by Jonathan Price
LIA - Emily Kilroy
MADDIE - Hannah Guterman
COAT-RACK - Amanda Horowitz

Full Circle by Wendy-Marie Martin
HARRISON - Johnathon Kidd Pollock
SYDNEY - Selina Alvarez
MEGAN/JADA/FRIEND - Sharon Rodas

Four Calls by Liz Shannon Miller
EMMA - Noelle Backman
JOSH - Gus Kamp

King's Gambit by Greg Machlin
CASSIUS - Henry Kamp
BLACK KNIGHT - Sareh Wilburn
BLACK ROOK - Alejandro Cervin
BLACK BISHOP - Hannah Guterman
WHITE ROOK - Josh Drummond
WHITE PAWN - Shir Zahavi
WHITE KING - Johnathon Kidd Pollock
WHITE QUEEN - Miya Parry

Jax-In-A-Box by Jeff Goode
DARIUS - Henry Kamp
JACKSON - Gus Kamp

GUTS

A short comedy by
Dave Ulrich

CAST OF CHARACTERS

ZOE, female.

DERRICK, male.

BUTT CHIN, male.

RATATOUILLE, male.

(A couple of outcasts, ZOE and DERRICK are hanging out. They have just finished lunch, alone on bleachers, away from everyone else.)

ZOE: Hey, when are you gonna get your tickets to...

DERRICK: *(Leaping to his feet:)* Whoa! Zoe! Check it out...

ZOE: What?!?

DERRICK: *(Pointing down, off into the distance:)* Fight!

(Two boys, BUTT CHIN and RATATOUILLE appear on the opposite end of the stage. They are circling each other slowly, fists up, prepared to fight.)

ZOE: Oh jeez. Who?

DERRICK: "Butt Chin" is about to kill "Ratatouille."

ZOE: Aww, I like Ratatouille.

DERRICK: That kid?

ZOE: Jeez Derrick, why would I nickname him after my favorite movie of all time if I didn't think he was all right?

DERRICK: Good point. But I thought it was 'cuz he kinda looks like... oh!

(Butt Chin finally throws the first punch. He hits Ratatouille in the stomach and Ratatouille falls to his knees.)

DERRICK: Ouch! Poor guy.

ZOE: *(Covering her eyes:)* I can't look. *(Beat.)* What's happening?

DERRICK: Butt Chin landed one in the gut. Oh, don't be ridiculous, Zoe. Just look.

ZOE: No, I can't look. Describe it to me...gently.

(Butt Chin resumes fighting position as Ratatouille gets back to his feet, stumbling back into his defensive maneuvers.)

DERRICK: If I'm going to be telling you, might as well see it yourself. They're mostly just circling each other, anyway.

(Zoe slowly lowers her hand from her eyes, but keeps the hand raised, in case she needs to cover again quickly.)

ZOE: I wonder what he did to Butt Chin.

DERRICK: I would guess that he breathed air and Butt Chin thought it was his air. You don't seriously think he did something.

(Butt Chin and Ratatouille each throw awkward punches and miss.)

ZOE: Boys are so dumb.

DERRICK: Like girls don't have bullies.

ZOE: We don't throw down.

DERRICK: Sometimes.

ZOE: Look — Butt Chin's trying to explain why he's gonna beat him up.

DERRICK: What's he saying?

ZOE: *(As Butt Chin:)* He's all like: "I'm secretly in love with my quarterback, so I'm going to hide it with a grand display of masculinity."

DERRICK: *(As Ratatouille:)* Haha. And Ratatouille is like: "I feel like my parents' divorce was my fault, so I deserve to be punched."

ZOE: That's awful.

DERRICK: No, what's awful is that whatever it is has nothing to do with Ratatouille.

ZOE: Well what is it, then?

DERRICK: It's like this...

(Derrick hops to his feet and takes a fighting position like Butt Chin.)

Take that! *(Punches the air:)* ... because I have a butt for a chin and I can't get rid of the zits on my face. And take that! *(Punches the air again:)* ... because I got these muscles from 'roids and I hate my tiny testicles. *(Punches the air again:)* And that's 'cuz even with summer school I might get put back a grade because I think studying sucks.

(Zoe jumps to her feet and gets in a boxing stance across from Derrick. They match the positions of Butt Chin and Ratatouille.)

ZOE: *(As Ratatouille:)* And OUCH! I'm gonna let you beat me up because everything makes me nervous, and I shovel food in my little rat mouth when I'm nervous.

DERRICK: *(As Butt Chin:)* And BAM! My older brother beats me up.

ZOE: *(As Ratatouille:)* And OUCH! I think about suicide.

DERRICK: *(As Butt Chin:)* And BAM! I'm scared of sex, but pretend I've already done it.

ZOE: *(As Ratatouille:)* And OUCH! I cut myself.

DERRICK: *(As Butt Chin:)* And BAM! I never talk to my parents except when we yell and fight.

(Butt Chin pushes Ratatouille to the ground. Derrick lowers his fists a little and takes a more serious tone.)

DERRICK: And I'm gay.

ZOE: Butt Chin? You really think....

DERRICK: No Zoe. I... well... I'm...

ZOE: *(Lowering her arms:)* Oh my god. So many things make sense now.

(Butt Chin walks a victory lap around the curled up Ratatouille on the ground.)

DERRICK: *(Dropping his arms completely:)* I don't know what to do.

ZOE: You don't know what to do?! I'm pregnant.

DERRICK: Wait. You...? No way!

(Zoe plops down and sits in defeat.)

ZOE: Way. As if I weren't a big enough loser, now EVERYONE's gonna shut me out.

(Butt Chin finally pounces on Ratatouille, and puts him in a headlock.)

DERRICK: *(Crouching down to comfort her:)* I won't.

ZOE: Yes you will. You still have a chance to fit in. You can't be seen with me when I'm preggers.

DERRICK: Fit in? *(Pointing down to Ratatouille:)* That's going to be me down there soon enough.

ZOE: Well, you hide it now. Just keep hiding it.

DERRICK: I don't think I can hide it anymore. I think it might even be harder.

(Pause.)

ZOE: So the social outcasts by choice are about to become social outcasts for real.

DERRICK: Well, you never know. Maybe this school will come around. Evolve.

(Butt Chin lets Ratatouille back up. Butt Chin walks a few steps away while Ratatouille dusts himself off.)

DERRICK: Actually, yes. Why not? We'll be the open-minded generation. A revolution that starts with us.

ZOE: Ha!

DERRICK: What do you mean, "Ha!"?

(Butt Chin goes back in and punches Ratatouille in the arm.)

ZOE: I mean who are we? We don't have the guts. We're sitting here watching someone get his face punched in—and mocking it.

DERRICK: Well what are we supposed to do? Go put our faces in front of a fist? Take that kid's place?

ZOE: I don't know. Maybe. Do something to stop it. Or go embarrass the bully.

DERRICK: Embarrass the bully??!!

(She slaps him.)

ZOE: Tolerating them is as bad as being one.

DERRICK: But...that's how the world works...

(She slaps him again.)

ZOE: Then change the world, Derrick! We can't watch from the stands anymore. We have to <u>be</u> the change.

(She attempts to slap him again, but he catches her wrist.)

DERRICK: You're right.

(Derrick lets go of her wrist, and turns toward the fighters. He takes a deep breath, and then runs the longest possible way over to the fight. Once he arrives, he turns back to Zoe and shouts to her as if he's shouting across a great distance:)

DERRICK: Vive la resistance!!!

(He turns back to Butt Chin and Ratatouille, then takes one slow-motion step into the middle of them...just as Butt Chin is throwing another punch.)

(Derrick accidentally, and quite comically, intercepts the blow with his face.)

(Zoe reacts with painful sympathy for her friend. But then she shrugs.)

ZOE: *(To herself:)* Personally, I would have tried words first. *(Raising a fist in solidarity and shouting back to Derrick:)* Revoluçion!

(Butt Chin and Ratatouille have stopped and are trying to understand what just happened.)

(Derrick struggles, but finally manages to raise a victory fist in the air from the ground.)

DERRICK: *(Weakly:)* Evolution!

(Lights out. End of play.)

The Author Speaks

What inspired you to write this play?
I have an over-developed sense of empathy—which is what drove me to be a writer and actor. That's why, even though I managed to avoid being bullied through excessive use of comedic timing, it was an issue that bothered me tremendously. I never felt I did enough to stop or prevent it. Now that I'm old and have become a father to a baby girl, I cannot help but think about her teen years ahead, and worry about the environment she will be forced to deal with. If I can write something that may help create change in schools before she arrives, then I feel I have to do it. I want every kid to be able to focus on what they need to be happy, and to feel confident enough to survive school without feeling lost and alone.

Was the structure or other elements of the play influenced by any other work?
I believe that everything we consume as moviegoers, play watchers, and TV addicts helps shape our own work. I can't think of a specific example, but the collective of many movies over many years probably helped this play reach the page. I could point all the way back to movies like *Pretty in Pink* and *The Breakfast Club*, I suppose—and more recently, *The Perks of Being a Wallflower*. These are the kinds of movies that send my empathy meter off the charts, and make me want to write something like *Guts*.

Have you dealt with the same theme in other works that you have written?
I think I always go for the downtrodden, the underdogs, the people with big hearts in rough circumstances. In *The Harvey Project* I styled a fellow that kept holding himself back from

accepting the true nature of the world around him, and therefore he couldn't move forward to get what he really wanted. In *The Passionates* it was a ragtag troupe of actors doing monologues of terrible people to try to make sense of the chaos they couldn't really handle...while the theatre collapsed around them. In *Guts* it's more of the same. These characters see the truth of the world they live in, but they don't know how to deal with it. Finally, they decide to take action, and try to change that world. Of course change is hard, so I wouldn't exactly say it goes well, but it's a start!

What writers have had the most profound effect on your style?

I would say Vaclav Havel would be a big one. I think *Memorandum* profoundly influenced the style of one world in my first full-length play, *The Harvey Project*. Even though I certainly don't write with his style, David Mamet has always driven me to keep my dialogue at a cadence and wording that's hyper-realistic—when I'm shooting for realism, at least.

What do you hope to achieve with this work?

I would love to have helped motivate the conscientious to shame bullies and free schools from their grip. Middle and high school bullies rarely go on to fulfilling adult lives, so it's tragic that their negativity can drive smart kids into dumbing themselves down, or unique personalities to blend. Bullies have driven the spark out of many people in a world that needs a lot of sparks.

What were the biggest challenges involved in the writing of this play?

I think it's the same challenge that any adult has when trying to put words in the mouths of middle or high school characters. First, how do you speak in a way that sounds genuine to actual school-age kids? And second, as an adult, you have to try to forget that you can see how these few years of school mean so little in the grand scheme of a whole life. Like so many others, I didn't get to truly recognize and become the "real me" until college. I have no love of my high school years—and pure disdain for my time in middle school. But you can exhaust yourself trying to get kids to understand that what they're living through now shouldn't be taken so seriously. But is very seriously to them. The here and now is everything, and they feel immortal as if they'll be in a four-year loop forever. As an adult writing as a kid, I have to temporarily forget all of the lessons that I learned over time and through my mistakes. And let my characters make their own mistakes and discoveries.

What are the most common mistakes that occur in productions of your work?
Timing. The dialogue should be snappy, and that alone will make pauses more dramatic and important. So many performances find actors trying to milk moments, and they ultimate become less funny than if they were played as I heard them in my head.

What inspired you to become a playwright?
In movies, anything you write is considered a rough piece of clay to be worked over and abused by development folks, punch-up artists, executive producers, and the actors' improvisation on the day. Novels require so much patience and planning. Playwriting lets you create compelling stories and examine the human psyche just through the way people communicate with each other. You can just dive right in and let the characters take the story in directions you didn't expect. And when you decide it's done, everyone actually accepts that it's done.

How did you research the subject?
I think simply living life gives everyone a context for bullying. Plus there are tons of movies and TV show that celebrate everyone who isn't a bully. And of course, there is Google.

About the Author

Dave Ulrich has written two full-length plays, two one-acts, and more than forty short plays. He also serves as a Playwright-in-Residence at SkyPilot Theatre in Los Angeles. His work has been produced and performed both in the United States and abroad to much critical acclaim. His latest (and third) full-length play, **The Golden Parachute** is now being reimagined as a musical after a staged reading. Away from the theatre, Dave Ulrich has also penned a children's book series, written and produced television shorts, is currently writing his first novel, and has had monologues appear in several collection publications. He has also spent more than a decade in the advertising industry penning ads for clients as big as McDonald's and Google.

SIX OF BEER

A short comedy by
Adam Hahn

CAST OF CHARACTERS

BRICE, male, a teenage boy.

MARK, male, a teenage boy.

NARRATOR

(BRICE and MARK hanging out on a couch.)

(NARRATOR in narration posture.)

NARRATOR: Two teenagers, on a couch, in a living room. Brice:

BRICE: Are you hungry?

NARRATOR: And Mark:

MARK: No. I'm thirsty.

NARRATOR: We will now show you six variations on one scene. All of them center around one thing:

MARK: Beer!

NARRATOR: Part one: Temptation. Variation One.

BRICE: What?

MARK: Your parents have a case of beer in the fridge. They won't notice if we drink a couple.

NARRATOR: Variation Two.

BRICE: What?

MARK: Twenty-four beers in the refrigerator. I bet I can drink more than you.

NARRATOR: Variation Three.

BRICE: What?

MARK: We have beer.

BRICE: We?

MARK: We should call girls and tell them we have beer. Beer plus girls equals party.

NARRATOR: Variation Four.

BRICE: What?

MARK: Beer.

BRICE: What?

MARK: Beer. Beer, beer, beer, beer, beer, beer, beer. Beer!

NARRATOR: Variation five.

BRICE: What?

MARK: You are a terrible host. I've been in your house for an hour, and you haven't offered me a beer. Stop being rude, get yourself in that kitchen, and pop me a cold one.

NARRATOR: Variation Six.

BRICE: What?

MARK: Do you want to drink some beer?

NARRATOR: Part Two: Reflection. Brice, stand up.

BRICE: What?

NARRATOR: You're going to tell us six different things that you might be thinking after your friend asks for beer. Stand here, so it doesn't look like a conversation with Mark.

BRICE: Here?

NARRATOR: Close enough. Number One.

BRICE: Even if we only take a few beers, my parents might notice.

NARRATOR: Number Two.

BRICE: If we drink as much beer as we can, my parents will definitely notice. Anyway, I have gym first period tomorrow, then a geometry test. I don't want to go through those hung over.

NARRATOR: Number Three.

BRICE: I do like the idea of having girls over, but the girls I'm interested in probably wouldn't be impressed by a random phone call asking if they want to get drunk on a Tuesday night.

NARRATOR: Number Four.

BRICE: Mark's not a good driver sober. If he drinks, then drives into a ditch or gets picked up by the police, he'll be in trouble, my parents will hear about it, and then I'll be in trouble.

NARRATOR: Number Five.

BRICE: I've seen Mark drink a couple of times. When he gets a little buzzed, he gets kind of annoying—more annoying than he already is. Then he keeps drinking, and he gets more annoying. Then he pukes. He'll be right in the middle of saying something really annoying, and all of a sudden he'll kind of—

NARRATOR: Thank you, Brice—

BRICE: Oh, and there's this sound he makes, like he's crying and puking at the same time.

NARRATOR: That's enough, Brice.

BRICE: And the smell! It's like he—

NARRATOR: Stop!

BRICE: Sorry.

NARRATOR: Number Six. Brice, have you ever even had a beer?

BRICE: No.

NARRATOR: Why not? Everyone else drinks.

BRICE: Not everyone. Actually a lot of people don't.

NARRATOR: Your parents do.

BRICE: But they're adults. They don't have to lie about it, and when they drink, they're careful.

NARRATOR: Don't you think you'd be careful?

BRICE: Yeah, in a few years. Have you looked at the kids my age who drink? Some of them do really stupid things.

NARRATOR: Don't they get away with doing stupid things?

BRICE: Sometimes. I don't want to lie to my parents, and I don't want to do anything stupid. I'm not ready to start drinking.

NARRATOR: Brice, go back to the couch, and we'll see six different ways Mark might react after you say no. Part Three: Resolution. Variation One.

BRICE: Mark, my mother notices if I don't change my socks every day. She'll notice if we take beer from the fridge.

MARK: Why would you not change your socks every day?

NARRATOR: Two.

BRICE: I don't want to drink. I have gym first period.

MARK: So a drinking contest will help you develop your competitive spirit. It's like studying for gym class.

BRICE: That's another reason not to do it.

NARRATOR: Three.

BRICE: We are not inviting girls over to drink my parents' beer.

MARK: This is why we don't have girlfriends.

BRICE: It's not the only reason.

MARK: That's fair.

NARRATOR: Four.

BRICE: No.

MARK: Beer?

BRICE: No.

MARK: Beer?

BRICE: No.

MARK: Beer?

BRICE: No.

MARK: Beer?

BRICE: Soda?

MARK: Beer?

BRICE: Soda.

MARK: Beer.

BRICE: Soda.

MARK: Soda?

BRICE: Soda.

NARRATOR: Five.

BRICE: No.

MARK: Give me one reason I can't have a beer.

BRICE: Mark, I don't like you when you drink.

MARK: I don't like you when you keep me from drinking. Get me a beer.

BRICE: I'm sorry. The answer is no. I don't drink, and I don't want you drinking here.

MARK: Everyone drinks.

BRICE: Not everyone—

MARK: I do! I drink, and you don't get to tell me not to. Why am I here? Why am I even talking to you? I put up with you not drinking as long as you stay out of my way. Now you're in my way. Get me a beer, or I'm leaving.

BRICE: Okay. After watching you throw a giant temper tantrum, I don't want you here.

NARRATOR: Six.

BRICE: No.

MARK: Why not?

BRICE: I just don't want to.

MARK: Okay. Video games?

BRICE: Video games.

NARRATOR: The End.

(End of play.)

The Author Speaks

What inspired you to write this play?

When a group of us started discussing the collection that would become *Pushed*, we brainstormed topics related to bullying and peer pressure. I was initially resistant to writing about alcohol. I was one of the few people I knew who didn't drink at all through high school and college. I didn't have a religious oath to uphold or a dramatic example of alcoholism in my family. I just didn't want to drink, and for years I felt a weird embarrassment saying no. Ultimately, writing about this topic was a way of exorcising that embarrassment. I had my reasons (some of these are mentioned in the piece: we all watch our friends do stupid things when they've been drinking), and exploring them on stage made them seem less trivial.

What writers have had the most profound effect on your style?

Among living playwrights, possibly Jeff Goode. He does an excellent job of blending serious content with zany humor, which is something I often attempt. My sense of theatricality probably takes as much from improvisational comedy as it does from scripted plays. That shows up in this piece through the use of the narrator who isn't just telling a linear story but guides the audience through alternate versions of the same scene. In improv shows, incredibly simple devices such as actors saying, "And now you're going to see..." let you jump several places in the space of a minute without the audience getting lost, and I try keep that flexibility in my work.

What do you hope to achieve with this work?

As always, honesty and humor. I don't want to lecture my audience with a warning that drinking can RUIN YOUR LIFE and you must SAY NO to protect yourself until your twenty-first birthday. I want to show a few relatable reasons that a character might decide not to start drinking tonight. I want to be honest about the effects of saying no to a peer (usually very little). I hope that I can do that in a piece that will make the audience laugh.

What inspired you to become a playwright?

I'm excited by the variety of ways that audiences and artists will engage with a script. A playwright creates essentially a half-finished piece of art. He relies on directors, actors, and designers to build on his foundation and create a new finished product in every production. As an audience member and an actor, I love productions that find new ways to bring text to life. As a playwright, I can't wait to see how a designer creates the physical world of the play or how an actor different from the one I'd imagined finds truth in the lines.

About the Author

Adam Hahn has been a Playwright-in-Residence at SkyPilot Theatre in Los Angeles since 2010. SkyPilot has produced his plays *Earthbound: An Electronica Musical* (written with composer Jonathan Price and lyricist Chana Wise) and *KONG: A Goddamn Thirty-Foot Gorilla*. His other plays include *Frogger, Dear Abe* (both first produced by Studio Roanoke in Roanoke, VA), and *Feedback Loop* (premiered at the 2010 Hollywood Fringe Festival). Adam holds an MFA from the Hollins University Playwright's Lab. As an actor, Adam has appeared in productions of the University of Iowa, in the Iowa Fringe Festival, and in the Piccolo Spoleto fringe theatre festival. He starred in his play *Dear Abe* at Studio Roanoke. He also performs long-form improv and is a graduate of the training program at iO West.

B-E AGGRESSIVE

A short drama by
Samantha Macher

CAST OF CHARACTERS

JANAE, female, a tenth grader.

ANA, female, another tenth grader.

OLIVIA, female, their cheerleader classmate.

CRYSTAL, female, Janae's sister, a senior.

DELANEY, female Ana's sister, a senior.

(Lights up on five high school girls. The two older ones, CRYSTAL and DELANEY, sit on one bench, two girls, ANA and JANAE, sit on another, and a third, OLIVIA is standing between them in a cheerleader's uniform.)

OLIVIA: Be aggressive!
B-E Aggressive!

JANAE: I can't believe she had the nerve to show up here.

ANA: That girl's got no shame.

JANAE: I know! Like she can walk up in here like a perfect little princess after what she did.

ANA: Seriously. She shouldn't have even been invited to that party. I mean, who even likes her?

JANAE: It's so unfair that she gets to go right back to being the center of attention and I can't even sit in the bleachers.

ANA: We could try again—

JANAE: No way. I can't deal with any more catcalling.

OLIVIA: B-E
A-G-G-
R-E-S-S-I-V-E
Aggressive
B-E Aggressive!

(She waves her pompoms.)

CRYSTAL: *(Pointing at Olivia:)* I can't stand her.

DELANEY: Me neither. Tenth graders are the worst.

CRYSTAL: Ever since that stupid party, Janae just hasn't been the same. This pep rally is the first time I've seen her out all week and that's only because she couldn't fake a fever. We never shoulda gone over there.

DELANEY: You were the one who took her? Girl, your mom is gonna kill you when she finds out.

CRYSTAL: I really thought it'd be okay. I thought it would be a fun way for her to meet my friends. I didn't even think there'd be beer! But no one's parents were home, and someone found out, and they brought the booze then all of a sudden: POOF—it's bad decision time. Now she won't even talk to me about it.

DELANEY: It's not like you guys talked before.

CRYSTAL: Yeah, but this is different. I had to find out from some girl in my English class.

OLIVIA: Go! Fight! With all your Might!
Explode, ignite, defense let's fight!

JANAE: God! Every time I see her ugly face I just want to punch it in.

ANA: You're prolly gonna have to wait in line. I hear she's got pics of Jackie and Xander but won't delete 'em.

JANAE: Well Jackie can just wait her turn. I want to break that girl's fingers. I want to make sure she never takes another picture again. That girl? She's nothing. She's less than nothing. She's a mattress with pompoms

ANA: That's one way to put it.

OLIVIA: Offense, offense, go run score!
Offense, offense, we want more!

DELANEY: Do you even know what happened?

CRYSTAL: Something about some boy and some pictures online.

DELANEY: Did you tell anyone? Your mom, maybe?

CRYSTAL: My mom? Are you kidding? She'd kill us both. Besides, she'd have to take time off work to deal with it.

DELANEY: What about Mr. Greenly?

CRYSTAL: The guidance counselor? What is he gonna do?

DELANEY: Maybe he can make Olivia take them down?

CRYSTAL: Don't you get it? They think that if some girl like Janae was "dumb" enough to do X, Y, and Z that she deserves what she gets.

DELANEY: I dunno, I mean it seems pretty reasonable to at least ask.

CRYSTAL: Delaney, please. It's like you don't even watch the news. Nobody out there cares about what happens to high school girls who go to parties.

OLIVIA: R-O-W-D-I-E
That's the way we spell Rowdy.
Rowdy, let's get rowdy!

JANAE: You know what we oughta do?

ANA: What's that?

JANAE: We oughta throw a party.

ANA: *(Sarcastically:)* Instead of beating her down? Yeah. That'll teach her.

JANAE: And we should have booze and invite boys —

ANA: Well, obviously, but —

JANAE: And when she gets good and liquored up, I say we give her a taste of her own medicine.

ANA: - -

JANAE: Isn't that a great idea?

ANA: I dunno. Janae. That seems like it might make things worse.

OLIVIA: Knock 'em down
Roll 'em around
Come on defense, work, WORK!

DELANEY: Maybe, but I think it's better than letting them handle this alone. I mean, they're like, fifteen. Who knows what they're gonna do?

CRYSTAL: Who cares?! It can't be worse than going to the school. Do you know what they'll put Janae through trying to get that picture down? What kind of questions they're going to ask?

DELANEY: Then you have to tell your mom and let her handle this. You can't let Janae go through this alone, and you definitely can't let these creeps get away with this!

CRYSTAL: She's gonna be pissed.

DELANEY: Yeah, well she's gonna be *more* pissed when she finds a picture of your sister on some website. That stuff gets around.

OLIVIA: Let's get physical
Get down
Get tough
Get mean
Let's get physical and beat the other team.

ANA: I don't know about this.

JANAE: What do you mean you don't know. It's *perfect!* Maybe she'll know how we feel for a change.

ANA: Can't we just kick her ass? I mean, seriously.

JANAE: I shoulda known.

ANA: You shoulda known what?

JANAE: You're just as uptight as she is.

OLIVIA: Hit 'em, Hit 'em
Smack 'em down
We are Central
We own this town

CRYSTAL: My sister wasn't even *awake* when she took that picture. Then she went and spread it all over school? That's not right, Delaney.

DELANEY: I'm sorry about that.

CRYSTAL: I just wish someone would have done something at the party. That someone woulda said something to help my baby sister. If I had known, I would have done anything to stop it.

OLIVIA: We are Central we know how to do this
C'mon girls we gotta get our boys through this!
Fight, fight, fight, fight
We won't rest til the end of the night.

ANA: I'm not uptight, Janae, I just don't think it's right.

JANAE: But you think it's right that she did it? That everyone around here knows everything about me? That every guy in school thinks I'll hook up with them now? That every girl thinks I'm a slut? Is that alright?

ANA: No. Of course not! But I don't think spreading this stuff around is the right thing to do.

JANAE: Then what do you want me to do? My life is ruined!

ANA: You gotta tell someone, Janae.

JANAE: Who am I gonna tell?

ANA: I'd start with your sister. I'm pretty sure she knows anyway.

(Janae is quiet for a moment.)

JANAE: You know what? I'm sorry I asked.

ANA: What?

JANAE: Get outta here, Ana.

ANA: Why? What did I do?

JANAE: Just leave me alone!

ANA: Fine! But I think what you're planning to do is wrong.

JANAE: Go away!

ANA: Whatever.

JANAE: That girl is gonna get what's coming to her.

(Ana walks over to her sister, Delaney, on the other bleachers.)

ANA: I'm not feeling so good. Can we go?

DELANEY: Yeah, sure.

(Delaney stands up.)

Bye, Crystal.

(Crystal looks off into the distance.)

OLIVIA: Be Aggressive
B-E Aggressive
B-E AGG-RESSIVE
Aggressive
B-E Aggressive

JANAE: Oh don't worry. I will be.

(End of play.)

The Author Speaks

What inspired you to write this play?
I was inspired to write this play after hearing about several of the incidents of students, both high school and college-aged, taking and distributing photographs of the sexual assaults of their classmates (e.g. Steubenville High School case). I was truly outraged by these acts and felt powerless in my ability to stop them. I thought as a writer, one of the best things that I could do would be to write a play about the emotional consequences and hope that when people read it, they feel a bit more empathy toward their classmates, and maybe take a stand if something like this is happening at a party they're invited to.

The only way that we can put an end to this kind of violence and bullying is to defend people in these situations. I hope that more students find the courage to do so.

Have you dealt with the same theme in other works that you have written?
This isn't my first time writing about assault, but it is my first time writing it for teens. It was a very interesting challenge.

What writers have had the most profound effect on your style?
A lot of my primary influences are other women writers like Sarah Ruhl, Marsha Norman and Naomi Wallace, but I also love a lot of new plays that inspire me as well. Some of the most influential playwrights (for my career) have been artists like Jeff Goode and Erin Courtney.

What do you hope to achieve with this work?
I hope to bring awareness to a subject that troubles me deeply and in doing so, help encourage people to take a stand against it should it arise.

What were the biggest challenges involved in the writing of this play?
I think dealing with the subject matter in a way that was delicate without sidestepping the issue was challenging. I think this is something that's always difficult to undertake when you have a play for young audiences. Teens and children are incredibly astute, so you want to be honest with them and the material, while simultaneously not offending their parents and teachers.

What are the most common mistakes that occur in productions of your work?
You can't perform my plays fast enough. One should only take a pause if it's going to change them in some way.

What inspired you to become a playwright?
I've always been a storyteller, but I decided to become a playwright when I realized that most of the stories I was telling were written primarily with dialogue. What excites me as a playwright (rather than a novelist or a poet), is exploring the way in which people communicate, most specifically, how they talk to each other. I love the English language. Exploring it in the context of conversation is always a fun challenge for me!

How did you research the subject?
I read a lot of articles that came out after the Steubenville High School case, among others. That was my primary method of research.

Shakespeare gave advice to the players in *Hamlet*; if you could give advice to your cast what would it be?
Your character is always the good guy, even when they're the bad guy.

About the Author

Samantha Macher is an MFA Playwright from Hollins University (Roanoke, VA), and holds a bachelor's degree from the University of Virginia in Religious Studies and Philosophy. During her graduate career, she has had several readings and productions, and is also a Reva Shiner Comedy Award Finalist. She is a Playwright-in-Residence at SkyPilot Theatre in Los Angeles, and a founding member of the Hell-Tro Theatre Collective (Brooklyn, NY). She has been a high school Latin teacher, an EMT, polo player, and guinea pig enthusiast, but is now a full-time writer. Her favorite color is pink.

FOAM

A short comedy by
Mike Rothschild

CAST OF CHARACTERS

MADISON, female, a popular high school student.

HUNTER, female, her friend, another popular high school student.

CHRIS, not their friend, an unpopular student.

HARVEY, a carrot.

(Lights up. MADISON and HUNTER, two popular high school students, stand center stage. They hold small, ornate containers.)

MADISON: This is so freaking good.

HUNTER: It's like...better than good. What's better than good?

MADISON: Um. Really good?

(They each sip from their containers, then delicately roll whatever they drank around in their mouths, making noises of intense pleasure.)

What do you have? I have jicama maple mango deluxe with a bacon reduction.

HUNTER: I've got seaweed saffron salmon sorbet. With a bacon reduction.

MADISON: Duh, Hunter. What's the point without the bacon reduction?

(They sip again, and make really loud and obnoxious noises again.)

(CHRIS enters, with a sack lunch and not anywhere near as much popularity. She takes out a sandwich. Madison and Hunter look at her in disgust.)

MADISON: What is that supposed to be?

CHRIS: Sorry?

MADISON: That...food. Is that a joke? It's not a funny joke.

CHRIS: I don't understand what we're talking about.

HUNTER: We're not talking. We're judging. Right, Madison?

CHRIS: Guys, come on. I'm just trying to eat lunch.

(She gestures toward her lunch.)

HUNTER: Exactly! I can't believe you'd put that filth in your body.

CHRIS: My sandwich? It's organic turkey on whole wheat.

MADISON: Carbs...regular nutrients. Ew.

(Chris nods, understanding.)

CHRIS: Let me guess. You guys are into foam?

MADISON: Who isn't drinking foam? Everyone important drinks foam.

CHRIS: Well, I'm not. Sorry.

MADISON: Like I said. Everyone important.

CHRIS: It's a fad. Foam is a fad. Just like the all the other fad diets, just like low fat, just like high fat, just like the positive molecular spin diet, just like the purple diet...

(Madison points an angry finger at Chris.)

MADISON: Do <u>not</u> throw shade at the purple diet! My mother lost thirty pounds on the purple diet.

CHRIS: I'm not going to stop eating food and start eating non-food just because you say it's so great. I need proof, not stories!

MADISON: Foam is better than food, stupid. It's made of super-nutrients, flavored anti-oxidants and hexagonal molecules that absorb better than regular round ones.

CHRIS: That's not a thing! None of those are things!

HUNTER: Have you even had foam?

CHRIS: No! Why would I try it? It doesn't do anything.

MADISON: You can't knock what you don't try. That's ignorant.

HUNTER: Like racism. Are you a racist, too?

(They menacingly walk toward Chris, who backs away.)

CHRIS: No! Of course not!

MADISON: Then why are you being racist against foam? Stop being stupid and TRY IT!

HUNTER: We're trying to help you through peer pressure and insults.

(Hunter thrusts a container at Chris.)

CHRIS: I don't want your stupid foam!

MADISON: Fat pig! Carb eater!

HUNTER: Food racist!

CHRIS: Fine, fine! I'll try foam! Just leave me alone!

(She takes the cup of foam and starts to put it to her lips.)

(Suddenly, a voice from offstage yells...)

HARVEY: *(Off:)* Stop that activity!

(HARVEY walks on stage. Harvey is a carrot.)

Before you make her drink that foam, think about what you're doing.

MADISON: Um....

HUNTER: Am I the only one seeing this?

CHRIS: No, we're all talking to a carrot.

HARVEY: Yes, I'm a carrot. And I am a carrot with questions. Why do you do this?

MADISON: Because foam is what people who care about their body drink. And we care about...whatever this person's name is.

CHRIS: Chris.

HARVEY: No, no. Not why are you making HER drink, why do YOU drink?

(Madison and Hunter look at each other. They've got this.)

MADISON: It helps you lose weight. Duh.

CHRIS: But how???? How does it help you lose weight?

HUNTER: It has hexagonal molecules...it does stuff. It's better.

CHRIS: Do you even know?

HUNTER: I...um...Madison, do you know?

MADISON: I thought you did. Look, I just saw someone drinking it and they said it made them thinner. That's enough for me.

HARVEY: That's enough? That's not anything! You have no idea what it does, but you're convinced that it does it, aren't you?

HUNTER: All I know is I feel great when I'm drinking foam. And none of your stupid questions can take that away from me, carrot.

MADISON: Yeah. It doesn't matter why foam works. It just works.

HARVEY: You two disgust me. You'll believe anything anyone tells you as long as it's insane, right?

HUNTER: We're not going to stand here and be disrespected by an ugly girl and a talking carrot.

MADISON: Especially not an ugly girl. Come on, Hunter. We've got foam to mindlessly consume.

(They saunter offstage. Chris looks at Harvey:)

CHRIS: Thanks for helping me with them.

HARVEY: Don't thank me. You asked the right questions. I just came out of nowhere to save you at the last second with no indication that I existed before that.

CHRIS: Right. And you're a talking carrot.

HARVEY: I am. And I don't want to discuss it.

CHRIS: I can imagine.

(Blackout.)

The Author Speaks

What inspired you to write this play?
I'm fascinated by the psychology behind fad diets and why people feel the need to use methods that aren't evidence-based to lose weight or improve themselves. I thought exploring this would fit well with the theme of peer pressure we were working with, and popular girls constricting their eating through some pop culture fad worked nicely. Many of the people who try to lose weight this way are doing so because of some kind of false notion of science or pseudohistory, often not even knowing why they're doing what they're doing — only that they should be doing it, and that anyone who isn't is not just wrong, but a fool.

Was the structure or other elements of the play influenced by any other work?
The talking carrot, Harvey, is named after the invisible rabbit in the play of the same name written by Mary Chase. Also, the idea of "hexagonal molecules" in food is a goof on the alkaline water craze, where complicated sciency-sounding word salad is used to make ionized water seem like a miracle curative for anything and everything. I also wanted to satirize the molecular gastronomy craze currently popular in high-end restaurants.

Have you dealt with the same theme in other works that you have written?
I write quite a bit about scientific skepticism and critical thinking, most especially blogging about conspiracy theories, scams, fads and urban legends. This work has influenced almost everything I've written for stage and TV in the last few years. I recently wrote a short play about the so-called "Denver Airport Conspiracy" for SkyPilot Theatre, and a recently screenplay I wrote revolves in part around the conspiracy

theory of government prison camps for dissenters. These themes, obviously in a much more youth-friendly presentation, are also part of this play.

What do you hope to achieve with this work?
I'd love kids to question the wisdom and efficacy of fad diets, and to approach food woo skeptically. It's become popular to discard evidence-based practices in favor of gut instinct and hearsay, and I believe this has a negative overall effect on critical thinking and reasoning. Ideally, a student who watches this play might think twice about the latest fad or hoax going around school and wonder what's really behind it.

What were the biggest challenges involved in the writing of this play?
It's hard to write about scientific concepts without either oversimplifying the science and talking down to people or not simplifying it enough and talking over their head. This goes double for young audiences. So I didn't want to get into any of the more complicated physiological or psychological aspects of fad dieting, and concentrate more on the "feelings" aspect of it. People do these things to lose weight, certainly, but also because it makes them feel like they're losing weight. This is something that can be written about without any technical jargon, but lots of funny, sciency-sounding gibberish.

What are the most common mistakes that occur in productions of your work?
My dialogue can be a little twisty sometimes, and sometimes actors paraphrase it if they get lost during a performance. I've seen it derail performances and send directors into fits. I try to simplify things where I can without losing the thrust of the jokes, but it can be a tricky line to walk, because in the end, a story like this only works if there's a certain amount of pseudoscience gibberish in it, and believe it or not, the words

used to represent that are carefully chosen.

How did you research the subject?
I found the most ridiculous sounding diets I could and tried to amp up the gibberish associated with them. Fortunately, I live in a place where you don't have to go far to find any number of bogus scientific and medical concepts peddled as self-care, and the bully characters in *Foam* probably will try them all at some point. I also read about the pop psychology behind so-called "historical" diets, and how people talk themselves into believing that they're based on ancient secrets, as opposed to bad science and marketing.

Shakespeare gave advice to the players in *Hamlet*; if you could give advice to your cast what would it be?
The two bullies should have supreme confidence that their liquid diet is the most amazing thing, but will have no idea how to describe why it's great or what's great about it. Chris should have a quiet strength about her, but clearly is also scared of being bullied and of asserting herself. And Harvey the Talking Carrot walks into every room knowing that he owns it, and that everything will revolve around him. Because he's a carrot that talks.

About the Author

Mike Rothschild is a playwright and screenwriter living in Los Angeles. He is a Playwright-in-Residence at SkyPilot Theatre, where he has written numerous works, short and long. He has also freelanced for many websites and media companies, and written several television pilots. His favorite cupcake flavor is red velvet, but wouldn't turn down something with chocolate, either. Follow him online at *rothschildmd.com*, or on Twitter at *@rothschildmd*.

OUT POST

A short drama by
Nicole B. Adkins

CAST OF CHARACTERS

CRUZ, female, a freshman.

ISABELLA, female, her big sister, a junior.

PRODUCTION NOTE

[Bracketed] text may replace the dialogue it follows, per director's discretion.

(CRUZ, a high school freshman, is in her room, pacing, talking on her smart phone.)

CRUZ: Mrs. Perez...yes ma'am...no, wait— I— could I talk to her for just a— please...I only want to tell her— *(Beat.)* Mrs. Perez? Hello? *(In frustration:)* AGGHH!

(She considers throwing her phone. ISABELLA, her older sister, watches her for a moment without being seen.)

ISABELLA: You OK?

CRUZ: *(Without looking up:)* Do I look OK?

ISABELLA: *(Beat.)* I'm making a nice dinner. Come downstairs?

CRUZ: I'll pass.

ISABELLA: Dad will be home soon.

CRUZ: *(Beat.)* Lea's mother just hung up on me.

ISABELLA: *(Beat.)* I'm sorry, sis...

CRUZ: Don't act all sweet! You have no right!

ISABELLA: I had nothing to do with any of this.

CRUZ: You sure didn't.

(She looks at her phone and then shows the screen to Isabella.)

Look. Look at all these comments on my page. It's been three days. Three days of nastygrams, notes in my lockers, messages from kids I don't even know wishing Lea and me dead... And my own sister? She says...nothing.

ISABELLA: They will get tired and move on.

CRUZ: To the next person?

ISABELLA: I asked Laura not to post anything else.

CRUZ: Oh, you "asked" her not to post anything else. How polite. Thanks.

ISABELLA: Not everybody is nasty like that.

CRUZ: Yeah but the ones who are speak loud. And you can't buy me off with sweet-talk and food! I'm not even hungry.

ISABELLA: I just wanted to — I was just trying to —

CRUZ: What I want is for you to have my back.

ISABELLA: I have your back.

CRUZ: Yeah, when things get tough, Iz'll put on her apron and make a nice dinner! A regular Betsy Crocker.

ISABELLA: It's Betty.

CRUZ: Who?

ISABELLA: Never mind. Anyway I cook when I'm upset.

CRUZ: What do *you* have to be upset about?

ISABELLA: Forget it.

(Isabella starts to leave.)

CRUZ: That's right. Avoid. Your best move.

ISABELLA: You're the one who said you didn't want to talk about it.

CRUZ: Well now I do. Let's talk about it. Let's talk about how *your* BFF gave everybody permission to open fire.

ISABELLA: She's not my best friend and yes, what she wrote was...terrible.

CRUZ: Off the map terrible.

ISABELLA: But, you're the one who posted the picture.

CRUZ: People post pictures with their friends all the time. If your BFF hadn't made that comment it would've ended there.

ISABELLA: I told you to delete it.

CRUZ: I don't negotiate with terrorists.

ISABELLA: You're kissing in the picture.

CRUZ: So? Who does that hurt? Anyway, it could have been a friend kiss.

ISABELLA: Nobody kisses their friends like that.

CRUZ: You and I used to kiss on the mouth.

ISABELLA: We're sisters. And it wasn't that kind of kiss.

CRUZ: I bet French people kiss on the lips.

ISABELLA: That was a French kiss all right!

CRUZ: Lea hasn't come to school in two days.

ISABELLA: And you think that's my fault.

CRUZ: This is her first time publicly going out with a girl. It wouldn't have taken much, Iz. One comment...or even just a like! I kept thinking that you were just thinking up the perfect thing to say, and it was gonna' be good...but then it was too late.

ISABELLA: So you start a war and I'm supposed to fight it for you?

CRUZ: I posted a picture of a kiss. Isn't that the opposite of war?

ISABELLA: That's not the point.

CRUZ: What is the point then? That I'm gross cause I like girls? What am I? Bigfoot? Newsflash fellow citizens: Lesbians

Walk Among Us. Watch out! They are Coming to Kiss You! What century is this?

ISABELLA: This isn't about that. Everybody at school's pretty much over that by now.

CRUZ: Oh yeah? Well that's not what all the comments on my page say. They tell me that plenty of people are still perfectly ready to hate me if other idiots, like your good friend, lead the way.

ISABELLA: OK, yes, some people are still living in the past. But mostly, people just like drama. They'll say whatever online. This is about Lea. She wasn't popular to begin with, and you gave everybody an opening.

CRUZ: What do you mean?

ISABELLA: *(Beat.)* You're the one who outed her.

CRUZ: It was one picture!

ISABELLA: Didn't it occur to you that everybody sees what you post?

CRUZ: When you posted those million pics of you and Tony you got like a hundred likes on every one. Everybody said how cute you were. Including me. Nobody tried to make you feel disgusting. And if anybody had I would have rolled over them like a tank.

ISABELLA: I didn't ask you to! And anyway this is different—

CRUZ: What's so different?

ISABELLA: Tony's and my relationship! Not because he is a guy, but... Look, you're supposed to love her, right?

CRUZ: I do!

ISABELLA: Well maybe going public with Lea's biggest secret wasn't the greatest way to show it.

CRUZ: I wanted her to see that I don't care how popular she is or isn't, I am still proud to be her girlfriend!

ISABELLA: You were making choices for her.

CRUZ: No! I was just trying to...make something *right*.

ISABELLA: I think you were tired of being kept a secret.

CRUZ: *(Beat.)* Yeah, so?

ISABELLA: You're a fighter, Cruz. You always have been. Why do you think Dad calls you his "like-it or-lump-it-kid"? I'm on your side. I always have been, but you and me, we are different. Maybe you gotta think sometimes about how you wanna make change.

CRUZ: *(Holding out her phone to Isabella:)* And maybe you need to act sometimes. If you are really on my side, log in and defend me.

ISABELLA: *(Beat.)* You and I have our own ways of doing things.

CRUZ: What? I do them, you don't?

ISABELLA: That's not it—

CRUZ: You've never complained about me fighting when it was in your favor. Like when you wanted to stay out past midnight for prom. I defended you. And when Grandma was gonna take out the hems in your skirts, I defended you. I convinced her to leave them alone. And look at the larger world—things never change unless somebody steps out and makes some noise!

ISABELLA: OK, but you can't make people change if they aren't ready.

CRUZ: Lea's the one who took the picture. With her phone! She texted it to me!

ISABELLA: To YOU! Not the world. Do you remember when you came out to Dad?

CRUZ: Yeah, worst day ever.

ISABELLA: Did you ever think that it might not have been so great for him either?

CRUZ: He's not the one who has to face life with people judging him for something he can't help!

ISABELLA3: Oh no? *(Beat.)* Why do you think we stopped going to Mass?

CRUZ: *(Beat.)* What?

ISABELLA: Dad didn't tell you why because he was trying to protect you. Sometimes that's what family does.

CRUZ: So...I shoulda just kept living a lie?

ISABELLA: I'm not saying that. But it'd be nice if you thought about your family sometimes. Do you know how many weird questions I've gotten? About our home? About how maybe you are who you are because our mom's not around... Or maybe somehow we "turned you" — like maybe it's our fault — my fault. That I should give you a makeover — or control you somehow.

CRUZ: So don't listen to them!

ISABELLA: Exactly what I have always told you!

CRUZ: Yeah, but the difference is, if somebody said anything like that to you near me I'd punch their face!

ISABELLA: You'd punch Grandma in the face? *(Beat.)* You...you make yourself a target. Couldn't you just lay low sometimes? Make things easier for yourself. Just right now — until you're on your own?

CRUZ: *(In disbelief:)* *Lay low?* What do you mean... like, be more like everybody else or something?

ISABELLA: That's not what I mean —

CRUZ: Oh I think you did. Sure. I'll just *lay low.* Fit myself right in with everybody else. I'll skip through the halls and gossip about nothing, and wear leopard print, and paint my nails, and go to dances with guys, and lie to everybody I meet so that I can make things easier for...who? Maybe you really mean, so that I don't embarrass my precious sister, so she can live some boring perfect life and won't have to feel bad about letting her dick [jerk] friends push me around. What next? You stand around cheering while Laura and her gang of trash kick Lea and me in our heads?

ISABELLA: That's not what I meant and you know it!

CRUZ: I thought high school was gonna be really good. Finally, after two years, I was back at the same school with my big sister. I was sure nobody would ever mess with me again, not with you around. *(Beat.)* You let me down.

ISABELLA: *(Beat.)* I'm sorry, and I want you to be happy. But it is not my job to defend you all the time. I never signed up for that. *(Beat.)* If you decide you want to eat with us, dinner will be downstairs.

(Isabella exits. Cruz sits on the floor. After a few moments, she takes out her phone and dials.)

CRUZ: Hello, Mrs. Perez?

(End of play.)

The Author Speaks

What inspired you to write this play?
While volunteering with an organization called The Book Truck that gives books to teens in underserved communities, I met a number of young women who were struggling with real-world problems for which their communities and culture didn't necessarily have a method of coping. Without the sense that the people they loved most understood them at all (or in some cases, cared), some of these teens really struggled with how to represent themselves in the world. I saw social media exacerbate this problem. I see it in the news all the time. The craving for positive attention and acceptance is never stronger than in our teen years—so the current ease with which we can post on the internet whatever we think or feel at the moment puts teens in a particularly vulnerable state. The onslaught that can follow these online decisions can be deeply damaging. I wrote this piece for those teens that have experienced this issue from any vantage point.

Have you dealt with the same theme in other works that you have written?
I often find myself writing about young people who are in the process of defining themselves, and/or who are exploring issues of personal responsibility. I also usually have a protagonist or a major character with a passion for a particular subject/career or intense drive of some kind, and another character who is struggling to find and articulate his/her own passion or niche.

What writers have had the most profound effect on your style?
I'm a greedy, voracious reader, and I believe that everything writers read shapes us to some degree. Some of the authors

whose work has stuck with me most include: Hans Christian Anderson, George MacDonald, C.S. Lewis, Ursula Le Guin, Douglas Adams, Terry Pratchett, Jane Austen, John Steinbeck, Shakespeare, and Suzan Zeder.

What do you hope to achieve with this work?
I would like to spark discussion about online bullying and how personal and/or social responsibility does or does not play into this issue, cultural stigmas, what we are willing to fight for, and where the responsibilities of family to one another begin and end. If the play starts a conversation, I'll be happy.

What were the biggest challenges involved in the writing of this play?
Cruz is a lesbian and she comes from a Catholic family. Since I do not have either of these things in common with Cruz, I really wanted to be certain that everything she said felt real and would resonate with an audience. I spent a lot of time talking with teens and other friends during the process of writing the piece who had more in common with Cruz. I also wanted to be sure not to paint Isabella as one-dimensional. I wanted to be certain that both sisters had genuine and relatable concerns and problems, even if I knew everyone wouldn't agree with every single thing each says or does. I do have a sister, and though our relationship is very different from the relationship between Cruz and Isabella, tapping into the love two sisters have for each other even when they are very different people was the simplest part.

What inspired you to become a playwright?
I have acted in theatre since I was four years old, continuing since as a writer, actor, teacher, set-painter, director, etc. I have seen time and time again how affecting theatre can be — for its

participants, and for its audience. I have also been writing and reading prolifically most of my life. These areas of interest have merged naturally over the years... I think I've always been a playwright. As to pursuing it professionally, I would really love one day to see original theatre for youth be as popular as books or even movies. I mean, why not? Theatre offers a completely different experience! I also think youth deserve plays that are as fresh, exciting, and dangerous — in the other words, as cogent, as the plays offered to adult audiences. I think everybody deserves theatre at its best. That is my aim as a writer: to make exciting theatre, encourage other writers to do the same, and to be a part of a larger movement and discussion.

About the Author

Nicole B. Adkins, Artistic Associate at YouthPLAYS, has worked with youth theatres for 16 years. She studied Theatre at the University of Central Oklahoma and London Academy of Music and Dramatic Arts, and holds a Master's degree in Children's Literature with an emphasis in Playwriting from Hollins University. Her plays have been performed at theatres, schools and museums, including Children's Theatre of Charlotte, NC; Creative Drama Children's Theatre in Winston-Salem, NC; Studio Roanoke, VA; The Young Actor's Studio of Los Angeles; and the American International School in Guanghzou, China. Awards include the 2011 Waldo M. and Grace C. Bonderman Award and recognition in the 2012 Beverly Hills Theatre Guild Marilyn Hall competition. A member of The Dramatists Guild of America, Inc., TYA/USA, and Alliance of Los Angeles Playwrights, Adkins has taught playwriting classes and workshops at Hollins University, Utah State University, and numerous other schools and organizations.

AWARENESS

A short dramedy by
Jonathan Price

CAST OF CHARACTERS

Three 15-year-old girls:

LIA

MADDIE

COAT-RACK, wears glasses, speaks quickly.

(LIA, MADDIE, and COAT-RACK enter. They carry light coats and backpacks.)

MADDIE: Not the art room again!

LIA: We're skippin' lunch. I didn't write my essay on bullying. This is the only time I got.

COAT-RACK: I didn't wanna skip lunch.

MADDIE: You wouldn't.

LIA: Suck it up, Coat-Rack. We got work to do.

(Lia takes off her coat and backpack. Coat-Rack extends her arms and Lia hangs them on her after taking out a notebook.)

MADDIE: My topic was "Bystander." I made my sister write it.

(She hangs her coat and backpack on Coat-Rack.)

You should make Coat-Rack write it.

LIA: Cooley won't buy it. She knows Coat-Rack's writing.

MADDIE: Use your tablet.

LIA: She knows her writing *style*. Besides, I forgot to charge it.

(Lia and Maddie sit down. Coat-Rack begins to sit down.)

COAT-RACK: Lia, Anime Con is...

LIA: Coat-Racks don't sit down.

(Coat-Rack stands back up, still holding all the coats and backpacks.)

COAT-RACK: Anime Con is a week from this Sunday in Costa Mesa and my mom said she'd drive us.

MADDIE: You should wait 3 months and Lia will have her license.

LIA: "Awareness." What the heck is awareness?

COAT-RACK: Well, my mom said she'd drive us, and there's a CosPlay, and I was thinking of going as Haruhi Fujioka.

LIA: *(To Maddie:)* I need a pencil.

> *(Coat-Rack takes out a pencil at the same time Maddie stands up to get one. Coat-Rack moves to hand her the pencil. Maddie backs away in mock horror.)*

MADDIE: Get away from me, perv! Get away!

> *(Maddie laughs. Lia snickers.)*

LIA: You fall for that every time. Hork it over to Maddie, Coat-Rack.

> *(Coat-Rack tosses the pencil to Maddie,, who then gives it to Lia.)*

COAT-RACK: I thought I could get a blue jacket and some dress pants from Goodwill, and get some shoes from there, like polish them or something, and get the tie and an iron-on crest online, cuz the whole costume is really expensive.

LIA: I can't write about awareness with a Coat-Rack jabbering in my ear! What am I supposed to write about anyway? If I see some jerks bullying somebody, I'm supposed to be aware. "Yep. There's a bully."

MADDIE: Did anyone bring a snack? I'm hungry.

COAT-RACK: I've got a granola bar.

> *(Coat-Rack pulls out a granola bar, while Maddie stands up. Coat-Rack moves to hand her the granola bar. Maddie backs away in mock horror.)*

MADDIE: Agh! Don't touch me! It's a pervert!

> *(Maddie laughs. Lia snickers.)*

LIA: *(To Coat-Rack:)* You are such an *idiot*.

(Coat-Rack tosses the granola bar to Maddie.)

COAT-RACK: Anyway, I was thinking I could get a brown, short-haired wig, and a wig stand, and there's a special brush you have to get for the wig and a hair net. With her glasses on, cuz she normally wears contacts but she *does* have glasses, so I'm just gonna be her with glasses cuz I don't wanna wear contacts.

LIA: Will you just *shut up*!

MADDIE: This isn't middle school, Coat-Rack. Nobody cares about CosPlay.

LIA: You are not allowed to say one more word! Got that? *(Lia stares at her notebook.)* I can only deal with one pain in my butt at a time.

(Coat-Rack dumps the coats and backpacks on the ground. She is upset and crying.)

COAT-RACK: You're supposed to be my friends!

(Coat-Rack runs off.)

MADDIE: She seemed, like, upset.

LIA: *(Looking at pile of coats and backpacks:)* What a mess.

MADDIE: I'm gonna go check on her.

(Maddie exits. Lia looks back at her notebook, unable to come up with an idea for her essay.)

LIA: "Awareness." I got nothin'.

(End of play.)

The Author Speaks

What writers have had the most profound effect on your style?
I was influenced by many of the playwrights who were part of the University of Iowa's Playwright's Workshop while I was a student: William Wallace Whitman, Glenn Blumstein, Ken Prestininzi, and Robert Hedley, to name a few.

What do you hope to achieve with this work?
I would hope that some audience members might re-examine what it means to be a bully and question how they treat others.

What were the biggest challenges involved in the writing of this play?
Trying to find suitable substitutes for the slang that was actually used by the real people the play is based on.

What are the most common mistakes that occur in productions of your work?
While Coat-Rack is the most sympathetic character, and Maddie has a very minor arc, the story is actually with Lia, the main bully. It's her goal to finish her paper that we track. She doesn't reach her goal because she isn't aware that she herself is a bully. This provides the final irony. Readings that have placed Lia as the pivotal character have succeeded very well. Those that focus on Coat-Rack's dilemma, as empathy-inducing as it is, tend to detract from the final irony.

What inspired you to become a playwright?
Both my parents directed high school plays, and some of my earliest memories are of sitting through rehearsals. Theatre and, by extension, opera are mediums that feel completely natural to me.

How did you research the subject?
A family friend had a daughter who was going through this.

Shakespeare gave advice to the players in *Hamlet*; if you could give advice to your cast what would it be?
Lia, be strong. Maddie, master the physical comedy of recoiling in mock horror. Coat-Rack, speak quickly.

How was the first production different from the vision that you created in your mind?
The workshop production at Determined to Succeed L.A. was very close to my vision. The actress playing Lia was very effective in playing the ringleader and making Lia a pivotal character. The actress who played Maddie had a great moment when her character realized that they'd been bullying Coat-Rack. And the actress who played Coat-Rack did a really good job of drawing our sympathy.

About the Author

Jonathan Price is the Senior Playwright-in-Residence at SkyPilot Theatre Company in Los Angeles. He holds a BA in Theatre Arts (with an emphasis in playwriting) and a BM in Composition from the University of Iowa, as well as a Graduate Certificate in Scoring for Motion Pictures and Television from USC. He directed the west coast premiere of Brett Neveu's *Detective Partner Hero Villain* and the world premiere of Samantha Macher's *Reset*. He is the composer and co-librettist (with Jeff Goode and Jan Michael Alejandro) of the award-winning opera *Æsopera*, the composer and co-lyricist (with Jeff Goode) of the family musical *Rumpelstiltskin*, and the composer of the scores to the films *Girl Meets Boy*, *Rustin*, and *Cyber Wars*. *www.jonathanprice.com*.

FULL CIRCLE

A short comedy by
Wendy-Marie Martin

CAST OF CHARACTERS

HARRISON, male, a 14-year-old boy with a desire to belong, preferably very Caucasian.

SYDNEY, female, a 14-year-old girl happy with who she is in spite of peer pressure, any ethnicity.

MEGAN/JADA/"FRIEND," female; roles are all written for a 14- to 16-year-old girl, preferably African-American.

(Lights up on SYDNEY and HARRISON getting seated at school desks.)

HARRISON: I'm serious, Syd. My brother told me—

SYDNEY: Well I think your brother's full of it. Why would you change anything just because we're freshmen?

HARRISON: Because this is the beginning of the rest of our lives, Syd. Do you really want to live the rest of your life like you are now?

SYDNEY: What's the matter with how I am now?

HARRISON: Forget it. Just don't come crying to me when you have no friends left.

SYDNEY: Whatever.

(Harrison exits. The bell rings.)

HARRISON: *(Off:)* Hut one. Hut two. Hut three...

(Harrison enters in a football jersey carrying a football. MEGAN enters in a cheerleader uniform.)

Hike!

(He pretends to throw the ball toward Sydney.)

SYDNEY: What the...are you crazy?

HARRISON: I was just kidding—

MEGAN: Good one, Harry—

SYDNEY: Harry? Wow. Who are you and what have you done with Harrison?

HARRISON: Very funny. I'm trying out for the football team after school—

MEGAN: Give me an H, give me an A, give me a double R—

SYDNEY: Don't make me hurt you.

(Megan exits quickly.)

Harrison, you hate football.

HARRISON: Not anymore. You are looking at the future star quarterback of the team—

SYDNEY: Oh my god, that is not going to make people like you—

HARRISON: Yeah? Well, we'll see, won't we?

(Harrison exits. The bell rings. Emo music is heard. Harrison returns emoed out.)

SYDNEY: Harrison? What happened to your football career?

HARRISON: It's dead.

SYDNEY: Oh. Well... I... uh—

HARRISON: We're all dying, you know. Every day. We die a little more.

SYDNEY: Oh my god. You aren't seriously—

HARRISON: Stop judging me, Syd, and worry about yourself.

(Harrison exits.)

SYDNEY: Whatever.

(The bell rings. Rap music can be heard and gangsta Harrison reenters with his new "friend," Jada.)

HARRISON: Yo, yo Sistah Syd. 'Sup?

SYDNEY: You need help, Harrison—

HARRISON: It's Killa H, now, Syd—

JADA: You tell her, Killa—

SYDNEY: Who is this person?

HARRISON: This here? Oh this is my good friend...Miss Juicy J—

SYDNEY: You're joking, right?

JADA: Watch yourself, girl—

HARRISON: She's cool, Juicy. She's cool.

JADA: If you say so. See you after class, Killa—

HARRISON: You know it.

SYDNEY: I think I just threw up in my mouth.

HARRISON: *(Dropping the accent:)* See? It's just like I told you. I've got a whole group of friends now—

SYDNEY: That was not a friend, Harrison.

HARRISON: You're just jealous.

SYDNEY: Whatever.

(The bell rings as Megan pushes a costume rack on-stage.)

(The next section should be underscored and choreographed so that Megan hands Harrison various costume pieces to signify his transformation in and out of various stereotypes. Between each change, Harrison poses in front of Sydney, who reacts openly. A bell rings between each transformation.)

STOP!

(Everyone freezes.)

This is ridiculous. Stop trying to be someone you're not. I can't take it anymore.

(Sydney exits. Harrison and his "friend" follow. The bell rings. Beat. Harrison enters back to normal. He sits and gets out his

notebook. A moment later Sydney enters, planning to sit somewhere else, until she sees him.)

Harrison? Is that really you?

HARRISON: Can't you tell?

SYDNEY: I wasn't sure. It's been so long since I've seen the real you—

HARRISON: Very funny.

SYDNEY: Gonna stick around this time?

HARRISON: Yeah. Wasn't really working out—

SYDNEY: You're telling me. *(Beat.)* I'm so glad you're back.

(Sydney kisses him on the cheek and sits down. A smile breaks across Harrison's face as the bell rings.)

(Lights fade. End of play.)

The Author Speaks

What inspired you to write this play?
When SkyPilot Theatre Company decided to create a collection of plays on peer pressure, I spoke with my teen daughter to see what issues the kids are dealing with and the idea of self-awareness and identity came into play. She mentioned how many kids change their "look" a number of times during their freshman year before finding the group in which they feel they belong. This led me to explore what cliques schools have today and then see how many of these one character could attempt to experience in a short play before coming to the conclusion that he's most comfortable being himself.

Was the structure or other elements of the play influenced by any other work?
The structure of this play is reminiscence of David Ives's play, *Sure Thing*, in that both reset the scene using a bell. In *Full Circle*, however, they do not reset to zero, but to another version of who Harrison could choose to be for his high school career.

Have you dealt with the same theme in other works that you have written?
I find the topic of identity fascinating and often explore it in my work. People have completely different levels of self-awareness and it's amazing to see how many people I meet who have a completely different experience of themselves than those of us on the outside. I'll probably never stop exploring this topic in my writing.

What writers have had the most profound effect on your style?
My time creating theatre in Germany had probably had the most profound impact on my writing style, more so in fact than any one playwright. I love to listen to stand-up comedy, too, which tends to influence the pace of much of my work. I love Jeff Goode's work, however, and find his ability to write heartfelt, honest comedy inspiring.

What do you hope to achieve with this work?
My hope is young audiences will see themselves in Harrison's struggle and realize that they do not need to change who they are to be liked or accepted. So many kids nowadays are afraid to embrace their originality and celebrate their unique contributions to the world. I hope they will realize by the end of the play that who they truly are is awesome, and they have no reason to want to be anyone else.

What were the biggest challenges involved in the writing of this play?
My biggest concern writing this play was being one hundred percent sure the voices of the characters were authentic and that the actors would be excited by the challenges of the play (i.e. extremely quick costume changes) and not scared off by them. I also wanted to find a way to keep space for the actors and directors to make creative choices while still giving them all the information they needed to create this world.

What are the most common mistakes that occur in productions of your work?
My work is fast. It has a quick pace and sometimes the stage directions may seem impossible, but they simply need the creative team to take a step back and find creative solutions. I find that sometimes the pace of the play isn't there and then

the comedy falls flat.

What inspired you to become a playwright?
I realized at the end of my acting training that I was having a hard time concentrating on the acting work because I was more intrigued by the thoughts behind the writing. I found myself wanting to rip open a monologue and rewrite it rather than work beats as an actor. Once I switched my focus from acting to playwriting, a whole new perspective opened up which allowed me to continue the acting work in my mind as I was writing. It's the best of both worlds.

Are any characters modeled after real life or historical figures?
These characters are modeled after a collage of high school kids I know, although I did have two specific actors in mind for the roles as I wrote them, so some of their idiosyncrasies are woven into the characters.

Shakespeare gave advice to the players in *Hamlet*; if you could give advice to your cast what would it be?
My advice would be to go crazy with the changes in this play to see how far you can take them. Don't start off limited by technical realities or what you believe may be limitations of space. There are many ways to stage the quick changes. Explore as many as you can before settling on your final choices. You can't be too big with this play. Sydney grounds the piece, which gives Harrison and his partner free reign to go overboard.

About the Author

Wendy-Marie Martin earned her MFA in Playwriting from the Hollins Playwright's Lab at Hollins University and holds a

BFA in Acting. She spent ten years writing, directing and performing in Europe. Her plays have been produced in Germany, The Netherlands, Australia, and the U.S. She is creator and co-Executive Producer of The Red Eye 10s Coast-to-Coast Play Festival, a nation-wide festival of new work. Wendy-Marie is a member of the Dramatists Guild, TCG, Playwrights' Center and is also a Playwright-in-Residence at SkyPilot Theatre Company in Los Angeles.

FOUR CALLS

A short dramedy by
Liz Shannon Miller

CAST OF CHARACTERS

EMMA, female, teenager, pajama-bound and doesn't care.

JOSH, male, teenager, looks cool, cares a lot about that.

SCENE 1

(Night. Lights up on EMMA and JOSH, both with cell phones. Emma is dressed for bed. She might even be in bed. Josh sits on a couch.)

(If possible, Josh's clothes change minimally between scenes — stripping down from a hoodie to a button-down to a T-shirt to a tank top. Emma's always remain the same.)

EMMA: How. Dare. You.

JOSH: Who is this?

EMMA: You're such a jerk.

JOSH: Seriously, who?

EMMA: You beat up my little brother today.

JOSH: *(Beat.)* I mean, honestly, who is this?

EMMA: My name is Emma. And my brother's name — your VICTIM's name — is Dave.

JOSH: Oh. *(Beat.)* I didn't know that was his name.

EMMA: You just beat up people you don't even know?

JOSH: Sometimes, yeah.

EMMA: Well, his name is Dave.

JOSH: And your name is Emma.

EMMA: And don't do it again.

(Blackout.)

SCENE 2

(Night. Same as before, Emma sitting up.)

EMMA: Hello.

JOSH: Emily? Wait. No. Emma.

EMMA: My brother told me you apologized.

JOSH: Well, I felt bad.

EMMA: Good.

JOSH: We're in the same class, aren't we?

EMMA: Yeah.

JOSH: Why don't I ever see you in school?

EMMA: I go to school.

JOSH: Yeah, but why don't I ever see you there?

EMMA: It's none of your business.

JOSH: Hey, you're the crazy person who keeps calling me. I figure you want to talk.

EMMA: I'm not crazy.

JOSH: Okay.

EMMA: Not. Crazy.

JOSH: Then what's the problem?

EMMA: I...I don't feel well. Sometimes. Most of the time.

JOSH: What, are you sick or something?

EMMA: Something like that.

JOSH: Is that why you call instead of text? Like, did your hands get cut off or something?

(A beat. Then, Emma laughs.)

EMMA: No. My hands are fine. I just... I don't talk to other people very much. It's nice to talk. Even when I'm talking to jerk bullies like you.

JOSH: I said I was sorry about that.

EMMA: But are you still doing it? Beating up kids like my brother?

JOSH: *(Long beat.)* I said I was sorry.

(She hangs up on him. Blackout.)

SCENE 3

(Night. This time, Emma is woken up.)

EMMA: Hello?

JOSH: Thank you for answering.

EMMA: I was asleep. I thought you were my alarm clock.

JOSH: Wake up. School starts in just seven hours.

EMMA: I don't talk to bullies.

JOSH: I'm going to keep calling you.

EMMA: Why? To explain why you terrorize kids? To apologize to the one person who doesn't care?

JOSH: If you don't care, why did you call me?

EMMA: Because I wanted to tell you to your face that you're a jerk.

JOSH: But it wasn't to my face.

EMMA: Goodnight.

JOSH: Don't—don't you want to talk?

EMMA: I can't. Not tonight.

(She hangs up. Blackout.)

SCENE 4

(Night. Emma is awake. Resigned.)

EMMA: Why do you keep calling?

JOSH: Why do you keep answering?

EMMA: Because no one else calls.

JOSH: That can't be true.

EMMA: You must have no idea what it feels like to be lonely.

JOSH: Of course I do. *(Beat.)* That's why it happens. With kids like your brother. It's how I make sure I'm not lonely.

EMMA: Don't blame me, my friends make me do it?

JOSH: They don't make me. They're just my friends.

EMMA: You need better friends.

JOSH: I'm working on that.

EMMA: That doesn't mean anything to my brother. Or the other kids you hurt.

JOSH: Does it mean anything to you?

EMMA: You want to be friends?

JOSH: I guess I just want to know why you don't come to school, if you're so lonely.

EMMA: You ever... You ever just feel like you can't get out of bed?

JOSH: Most mornings, yeah.

EMMA: Well, that's me. All the time.

JOSH: So you just don't?

EMMA: Pretty much. I mean, who cares, right?

JOSH: Your brother does.

EMMA: You talk to him about me? *(Beat.)* Wait—you guys talk?

JOSH: Yeah, at lunch and stuff. You know. He's all right, once you get to know him.

EMMA: Yeah. He's great.

JOSH: You should come to school. Have lunch with us.

EMMA: This isn't something I can just snap my fingers and fix.

JOSH: But you must want to.

EMMA: Why do you say that?

JOSH: Because you called me. Remember? Twice.

EMMA: And now you're my alarm clock.

JOSH: Yep.

EMMA: *(Long beat.)* You want to see me?

JOSH: Yeah. Put a face to the name. Put a face to the angry voice.

EMMA: I'm not mad at you anymore.

JOSH: You aren't?

EMMA: Yeah.

JOSH: Good. I'm glad.

EMMA: Okay.

JOSH: Okay what?

EMMA: See you in school.

   (Blackout.)

The Author Speaks

What inspired you to write this play?
When asked to write a play about the subject of bullying, I was intrigued by the idea of pairing your stereotypical bully with someone who can't stop beating herself up. I was also struck by the memory of a good friend of mine from high school, who'd be absent for days at a time; it took me months to learn that she was missing school because of acute depression. I remember how helpless I felt when I'd see she was absent again—I'd reach out as best I could, but that only really works if the person you're calling answers the phone. Reaching out for help is so hard when you're coping with depression— writing this was a way of reaching back through time, and giving her that strength.

Was the structure or other elements of the play influenced by any other work?
It's intended for a very different audience, but *Closer* by Patrick Marber came to mind when approaching it as a two-hander.

What writers have had the most profound effect on your style?
I grew up reading everything from Shakespeare to comic books, but easily my biggest early influences actually came from television writers, from Joss Whedon to Aaron Sorkin. But later, thanks to the influence of screenwriters like Kevin Smith, I became fascinated by writing dialogue that genuinely sounds like human speech. The most important part of the playwriting process, for me, has become rehearsals and readings of my work, because getting a chance to hear actors say the words out loud means a chance to weed out the artificial lines. Oftentimes, the most valuable moments come

from when an actor misspeaks a line as written—instead finding a more natural way of saying it. In short, currently the writers who have the most profound effect on my style are the actors I'm lucky enough to work with directly.

What do you hope to achieve with this work?
Hopefully, it creates a character, in Josh, that makes people understand one reason why a decent guy might turn to bullying. And also gives those who struggle with depression a character to identify with—Emma isn't cured at the end, but the struggle is what matters.

Most importantly, I'd like to keep the concept of the phone call alive. Texting is fine, but there's something to be said for the long late-night phone chat.

Are any characters modeled after real life or historical figures?
Emma was inspired by my high school friend; I also couldn't help but think of her unseen brother as my own younger sibling.

Shakespeare gave advice to the players in *Hamlet*; if you could give advice to your cast what would it be?
Remember what it's like to share a secret in the dark. Remember how being anonymous can also make you much more honest.

About the Author

Liz Shannon Miller is a writer for stage, screen and the web, having worked as a staff writer on G4's *Attack of the Show* and currently serving as TV Editor of *Indiewire.com*. She has a BFA in screenwriting from USC, and has been published by the

New York Times, Variety, The Wrap, Nerve and Thought Catalog. Based in Los Angeles, she has been a Playwright-in-Residence with SkyPilot Theatre since 2010: Produced theatre works include the critically acclaimed **Lights Off, Eyes Closed** (SkyPilot Theatre), as well as the one-acts **Something Biblical** (Sight Unseen Theatre), **Ideation** (3 of a Kind Theatre), **Negotiations** (Black Box Theatre), and **Judgement** (SkyPilot Theatre). For more information, visit *lizshannonmiller.com.*

KING'S GAMBIT

A short drama by
Greg Machlin

CAST OF CHARACTERS

CASSIUS, 15, high school freshman who identifies as transgender.

<u>Black Chess Pieces (Cassius' Team)</u>

BLACK KNIGHT, preferably female, tough, younger.

BLACK ROOK, either, slower and older.

BLACK BISHOP, either, cautious.

<u>White Chess Pieces (Opposing Team)</u>

WHITE PAWN, either, young, obnoxious.

WHITE QUEEN, female, older, exceedingly dangerous.

WHITE KING, male, older, unfocused.

PRODUCTION NOTE

[Bracketed] text may replace the text it follows, per director's discretion.

(CASSIUS' bedroom. He's 15, a freshman in high school. A banner for Central High School is taped to the wall.)

(Actors representing four white pieces and three black ones are in the final stages of a chess game. Chess piece characters wear all white or all black clothes, with something visible to clearly indicate their piece. Even when the pieces played by actors aren't moving/active, they're alert, concentrating on the game — or on Cassius.)

(Directors do not have to match the board squares referenced in stage directions; it's just important that it feel like a chess game.)

CASSIUS: Trans: adjective. "Used to describe anyone whose identity or behavior falls outside of stereotypical gender norms. More narrowly defined, it refers to an individual whose gender identity does not match their assigned birth gender." *(To himself:)* Speak English, Cassius! Someone in a man's body who identifies as a woman. Or someone in a woman's body who identifies as a man. Different from gay — a guy who's gay has no problem with being a man — he's just attracted to men instead of women. But people who are trans are convinced they're trapped in the wrong body. Many people who can afford it get surgery to change their gender when they're grown up. My parents would never allow that.

(He moves to the chessboard to consult with his pieces, the black ones.)

BLACK KNIGHT: A wise man once said "I make my own luck." As a knight, I agree. They never see me coming.

BLACK ROOK: You know, Ruy Lopez told me about a situation like this back in 1673…

BLACK BISHOP: You never knew Ruy Lopez, Black Rook! For crying out loud, will you shut up about Ruy Lopez? It's "Ruy Lopez" this and "Ruy Lopez" that!

WHITE PAWN: Hey, tell your fat rook friend to shut up, fatty!

(White Pawn moves, stepping forward.)

BLACK BISHOP: And…I'm movin' back this way.

(Black Bishop moves a square.)

BLACK ROOK: If you were in my sightlines, I'd take you out, you creepy little pawn!

WHITE PAWN: But you're not, are you, fat man? Lard ball? Tubbo?

BLACK BISHOP: *(Pointing at the White Pawn:)* Keep your eye on him!

BLACK ROOK: *(Pointing at the White Queen:)* Do you *see* the giant White Queen in front of me? I'm a little tied up right now! She could take me at any minute!

WHITE QUEEN: Cassius, I don't understand. You say you wish you were a woman? That doesn't make any sense. *(Concerned for him. Not malicious:)* You're sick, sweetie. You just need to see a doctor and this strange phase will pass.

BLACK KNIGHT: Hey. Leave the kid out of it. Game's on the board.

WHITE QUEEN: The game's everywhere.

WHITE PAWN: Yeah, Cassius knows that. Don't you, Cassius? See, I've been thinking about your problems. Nobody's going to listen to your crazy, weird, I-identify-as-female stuff. That's way worse than being gay. YOU WILL HAVE NO FRIENDS if you try and tell anyone else about this. So —

BLACK KNIGHT: Cassius, don't listen. He's dangerous.

(White Pawn jumps a square forward.)

WHITE PAWN: You can hear them talking about you in the halls, in between classes. They *already* think you're gay. How many "sick days" you used up this year. Seven? And it's only October! I have a solution: you should consider killing yourself.

(Pause.)

CASSIUS: I've thought about that.

WHITE PAWN: Then everyone would feel sorry for you. And you wouldn't have this whole weird thing that you had to hide away —

(White Pawn jumps forward.)

—from your friends, your mom, your dad. Your mom said you could talk to her about anything…but clearly, she lied.

BLACK ROOK: Cassius, little help!

(The Black Rook steps to one side to avoid the White Pawn.)

CASSIUS: I need to make sure my king's safe.

WHITE PAWN: Gee, that's a shame.

(Jumps onto the final row/rank:)

Because now I get to turn into a queen.

CASSIUS: *(Smiling:)* I'm sorry, did you say you wanted to become female?

WHITE PAWN: Of course not! You're the one who wants to wear a dress. That, and get the, uh, equipment. Not me. *(Pointing at his crotch:)* I have never met a guy who wanted to get rid of that. You gonna wear pink now? Play with those "American Girl" dolls?

CASSIUS: No. And I don't know any 15-year-old girls who do that. You hate girls?

WHITE PAWN: Not *real* girls. I *love real* girls. But men who want to turn themselves into girls—you gotta admit, there's something wrong there. So, no, I'm not going to wear a dress. Fag. [Gay-boy.]

CASSIUS: Bigoted much? I'm not gay. I'm trans. There's a difference.

WHITE PAWN: No real man would want to be a woman ! It's sick!

CASSIUS: In that case, you probably don't want to turn into a queen.

WHITE PAWN: Well, I'm not going to be a rook! Rooks are fat!

BLACK ROOK: Just pick *something.*

WHITE PAWN: Fine! I want to be a bishop! A promotion is a promotion! We're gonna beat you anyway.

(*White Pawn picks up a pointy bishop's hat.*)

BLACK KNIGHT: Wrong move.

(*Black Knight jumps closer to the White King.*)

Check.

WHITE KING: Oh, you stupid useless waste of plastic, White Pawn!

WHITE PAWN: Sorry, Dad!

(*White King stomps backwards.*)

BLACK KNIGHT: Back where I come from, threatening two pieces at once—we call that a fork.

WHITE PAWN: Hey, all that stuff I said about Cassius—I know he's your little brother—I didn't mean it.

BLACK KNIGHT: Of course not.

(Black Knight jumps onto the same square as White Pawn:)

Just like I don't mean this sleeper hold.

(Black Knight puts White Pawn in a sleeper choke hold. White Pawn struggles, then collapses. Cassius drags White Pawn off board.)

BLACK ROOK: And that's a *stupid hat!*

BLACK BISHOP: Ahem.

BLACK ROOK: *(To Black Bishop:)* Uh, no offense. Your hat is... totally different.

WHITE QUEEN: Cassius, honey, have you ever considered that this whole "transgender" thing is just a bid for attention? Listen, I'm sorry we've been so busy with the law firm and everything, but this is *sick—*

CASSIUS: I *am* sick! I'm sick of pretending to be someone else! I'm a woman, okay?

WHITE QUEEN: You listen to me, young man. If you wear a dress to school, I will ground you for the rest of your life. And take away your internet. That's where you got this stupid idea, anyway.

(The White Queen storms over, close to the Black Knight.)

BLACK KNIGHT: Did you forget I move in an L-shape? And *backwards?*

(The Black Knight jumps in an L-shape to land on the same square as the White Queen.)

Take her away, boys.

WHITE QUEEN: Cassius, you can't do this! Think of what you're doing *to me!*

(The White Queen, hissing and muttering, scurries off the board.)

WHITE ROOK: Guys, it's okay. Cassius is their leader! They can't win with him! Cassius, what's it like being a girly loser? I'm totally gonna take your knight out.

(White Rook slides over and grabs onto the Black Knight.)

I'm going to enjoy this.

BLACK BISHOP: Really? Take another look at the board. You just left your king in check. From me. ILLEGAL MOVE. Move back to where you were.

WHITE ROOK: Uh… Uh…

(Ashamed, he scurries back. The move must be replayed.)

WHITE KING: I am surrounded by idiots.

CASSIUS: You need to redo the move.

(White King moves to a different square [f6].)

BLACK ROOK: Cassius, you know there's a famous British comic called Eddie Izzard who wears a dress every time he goes onstage?

CASSIUS: I didn't. Is he trans?

BLACK ROOK: No, but Lana Wachowski, who wrote and directed *The Matrix* with her brother, is.

BLACK BISHOP: Time to go, White Rook.

(Black Bishop moves from b3 to e6 to take White Rook.)

WHITE ROOK: *(Like Bill Paxton in* Aliens:*)* Aw, no, man, no, no, no! That's game over, man! Game over!

(White Rook slumps off the board.)

BLACK KNIGHT: *(Moves to c6:)* So what happens next?

CASSIUS: *(Deep breath:)* I announce that I'm trans at school. Tomorrow.

BLACK ROOK: Are you ready for what's ahead?

CASSIUS: I don't know. I really don't. I'm terrified.

(White King edges away from them:)

WHITE KING: Look, I didn't *mean* it! Can we call it a draw?

(Black Rook races forward to h7:)

BLACK ROOK: You can run, but you *cannot* hide. *Check.*

WHITE KING: Mercy! For the love of God, mercy!

BLACK ROOK: Were you going to show Cassius mercy?

WHITE KING: Well, no—but still!

(Cassius stands up. All pieces except Black Knight and White King return to stillness.)

BLACK KNIGHT: Good luck, kid. You're gonna need it.

CASSIUS: I know. But 'round these parts, I make my own luck.

(Black Knight freezes.)

WHITE KING: You can't checkmate me! You don't have a black queen! I survive to sneer at you another day!

(Cassius takes off his shirt, reaches into his closet, pulls out a dress, and pulls it on.)

CASSIUS: I'm the Black Queen. I've been hiding down at d1 this whole time. Didn't see me? Look again. Black Queen slides all the way to d8. *Checkmate!*

(Lights down. End of play.)

The Author Speaks

What inspired you to write this play?
The indefatigable Nikki Adkins (director of educational outreach at SkyPilot) organized a reading of ten-minute plays about peer pressure by SkyPilot playwrights. I'd recently finished four years working as a chess teacher to elementary school students, so I combined the chess and the peer pressure and came up with *King's Gambit*. That's the great thing about being in a company dedicated to creating new work—there's always a chance to make more of it.

Was the structure or other elements of the play influenced by any other work?
I'm certainly not the first writer to use the objects or game-pieces-standing-in-for-real-life-people concept. I can't remember specific examples at the moment—*Alice in Wonderland?*—but there are definitely other works out there that do something similar. The best chess-pieces-come-to-life book I know is *The Squares of the City* by John Brunner.

Have you dealt with the same theme in other works that you have written?
My ten-minute play *Family Portrait* deals with the tragic aftermath of a teenage suicide; luckily, Cassius is more resourced than that. On a lighter note, inanimate objects coming to life is a favorite topic of mine—*Sushi* is my most-produced ten-minute play.

What writers have had the most profound effect on your style?
I get my bizarre sense of humor from my dad and my writer's discipline from my mom, who managed to write a novel while raising two kids, one of whom kept asking her when her novel

would ever be done. Christopher Durang's wild sense of humor and David Ives' perfectly crafted, hysterically funny one-acts were early influences. My collaborations with my frequent director and partner in crime Joe Luis Cedillo have had a significant impact on my later work, as I've explored darker and more realistic themes. In the film and TV world, Joss Whedon, Kasi Lemmons, Charlie Kaufman, and Darin Morgan (who wrote the brilliant *X-Files* episode *Jose Chung's From Outer Space*) were all hugely impactful.

What do you hope to achieve with this work?
My ambitions are modest. I hope that students who perform the play and/or see it gain a better appreciation of the difficulties transgender students have.

What were the biggest challenges involved in the writing of this play?
Time—I sometimes overextend myself and was working on several different projects through the various drafts. Time management is your friend.

What are the most common mistakes that occur in productions of your work?
People definitely overplay the comedy or try to make things funnier (not much chance of that here, since **King's Gambit** is more dramatic, but it's definitely been an issue with **Bloody Lies** and a play titled, ironically enough, **The Collaborative Process**). Actors and directors should relax, and just ground the work in real emotions and specific actions. If the script is wild and comedic, it'll do the heavy lifting for the funny. You just have to be truthful.

What inspired you to become a playwright?

I was an actor for 10 years (ages 12 to 22) and, while in college, discovered that I got way more attention for the short comedy sketches I was writing than my mediocre auditions, and I'd always been some kind of writer, so I made the switch. Kids, theatre is a drug. Use with caution.

How did you research the subject?

I have friends who have transitioned from female to male and male to female (one of whom acted in a play I directed at Iowa), so I have a small sense of what they've gone through. I read up on the experience of transgender people who transition on various sources. I hope I've succeeded in portraying what a high-school student in this situation might actually go through.

Are any characters modeled after real life or historical figures?

No, although Ruy Lopez — mentioned in the play — was a real and famous chess player, and comedian Eddie Izzard and filmmaker Lana Wachowski are also real people.

Shakespeare gave advice to the players in *Hamlet*; if you could give advice to your cast what would it be?

(Note: I think Shakespeare may have been satirizing civilians' tendency to give unnecessary advice to actors, but that's just me.) Work hard, come to rehearsals *on time,* respect the time of your fellow actors, *respect and thank anyone and everyone working backstage,* and be focused and present for all of rehearsal. Don't worry too much about performance; if you've done the work, you'll do well.

What do you think poses the greatest danger to humanity?

Bees.

No, bears.

No, bees and bears that LEARN TO TEAM UP. LOOK OUT, WORLD.

About the Author

Greg Machlin received his MFA from the Iowa Playwrights' Workshop and is a Playwright-in-Residence at SkyPilot Theatre, which recently staged a workshop production of **Keith Haring: Pieces of a Life,** a full-length play authorized by the Haring estate; six out of eight performances sold out. He was a Heideman finalist for his ten-minute **Family Portrait** and won the TUNY award for Best 24-hour play from Theatre Unleashed for **Smart Phone.** His work has been produced in several states, broadcast on NPR, and published by Smith & Kraus. His comedic vampire love story **Bloody Lies** was a Best New Script finalist at the Midtown International Theatre Festival; he was a Samuel French Finalist. Most recently, he was a writer/producer on *LA Beer,* the world's first multi-cam web series. With David Butler, he created the comedy web series *WRNG in Studio City* about reporters forced to make up fake news. He lives in LA.

JAX-IN-A-BOX

A short comedy by
Jeff Goode

CAST OF CHARACTERS

DARIUS, male, an older brother.

JACKSON, male, a younger brother.

(Lights up on a large cardboard box. Enter DARIUS, dribbling a basketball. He notices the box, decides to ignore it, at first. After a while, though, he dribbles closer.)

DARIUS: Is that you, Jax?

JACKSON: *(From inside the box:)* Go away.

DARIUS: What are you doing?

JACKSON: I said, "Keep walking!"

DARIUS: Aren't you supposed to be in school?

JACKSON: Aren't you?

(Darius dribbles in silence.)

DARIUS: Does your mom know you're in a box?

JACKSON: What do you care? You're not my brother no more.

DARIUS: Maybe not, but I bet your mom'd care if she found out you was cuttin' class. *(Pause for effect.)* Might even give me a reward for turning you in.

JACKSON: I'm not going back to that school!

DARIUS: I hear that.

JACKSON: Ever.

DARIUS: I thought you liked school.

JACKSON: Who told you that?

DARIUS: You get good grades.

JACKSON: So?!

DARIUS: Better than I get.

JACKSON: That basketball gets better grades than you get.

DARIUS: Don't make me come in there, Jackson.

JACKSON: The only thing I like about that school is from now until three o'clock, everyone in the world that hates my guts is inside that building. And as long as I stay out of it, they can't get me.

DARIUS: Kids pickin' on you again?

JACKSON: Again? They don't stop, Darius!

DARIUS: So how do you think it's gonna go if they see you hiding in a box?

JACKSON: They can't see me, if I'm in here. That's the point, stupid.

DARIUS: You gotta watch your mouth.

JACKSON: The only thing they're gonna see is some idiot skippin' class so he can talk to a box.

DARIUS: All right, that's it, you're comin' out!

(Darius plunges his hand into the box. And quickly pulls it back out.)

Ow! You cut me!

JACKSON: I scratched you. Don't be a baby.

DARIUS: I'll show you who's a baby!

(Darius plunges both hands in the box. And just as quickly pulls them back out.)

Ow! Knock it off!

JACKSON: I'm not comin' out!

DARIUS: Fine, stay in there.

JACKSON: I will!

DARIUS: You need to cut your fingernails.

JACKSON: I did. And then I sharpened them.

DARIUS: You what?? Why'd you do that?

JACKSON: Cuz it's the only thing keeps people from grabbin' at me.

DARIUS: That's stupid.

JACKSON: You gonna stick your hand in here again?

DARIUS: No.

JACKSON: Then it's working.

(*Darius dribbles, considers leaving.*)

DARIUS: You can't stay in there forever, Jackson.

JACKSON: Not forever. Just until I graduate high school.

DARIUS: You're not gonna graduate if you don't come outta your box.

JACKSON: All I need is a D minus.

DARIUS: Everybody hates school, Jax, but we all gotta go. You think I like it in school?

JACKSON: You don't like it cuz you're bad at it. I don't like it cuz they all want me dead.

DARIUS: What? Nobody wants you dead.

JACKSON: Then I don't know where I heard it.

DARIUS: You think the whole school's tryin' to kill you?

JACKSON: I didn't say that. I said they want me to die. They say it to my face.

DARIUS: They don't say you should die.

JACKSON: And send me links to suicide kids like I should take a hint.

DARIUS: You're makin' that up.

JACKSON: I'm not makin' it up, Darius! Just cuz you don't wanna see it, don't mean it's not happening! That's why they do it! Cuz they think you're okay with it.

DARIUS: I never said it was okay.

JACKSON: No, you don't have to say nothin'. Just stand there and watch. *(Pause.)* Be nice if somebody had my back.

DARIUS: So all this is cuz you're afraid to go to school?

JACKSON: I'm not afraid!

DARIUS: You're hidin' in a box.

JACKSON: I tried to go. I can't. I get sick to my stomach.

DARIUS: You get sick being at school?

JACKSON: It's like I can't breathe. My hands start shaking. I tried to go today and I had to throw up in the parking lot.

DARIUS: Aw, no, yuck. Did anybody see you?

JACKSON: I don't know. I ran away.

DARIUS: Well, I guess you did the right thing. You don't want people finding out about that.

JACKSON: And the farther away I ran, the better I felt. Until I got here and I crawled in this box. And now I'm fine. As long as I stay in here, I'm fine.

DARIUS: You're not fine. You're in a box. This isn't fine.

JACKSON: It's quiet. There's nobody here to tell me what they think of me.

DARIUS: You gotta come outta there sometime, Jax. Look, you don't see me skippin' school just cuz I don't keep up in my classes. And all my teachers ridin' me cuz I can't get the same grades as my little brother.

(Jackson pokes his head out of the box for the first time.)

JACKSON: *(Suspicious:)* You're right. You don't care about any of that.

DARIUS: That's what I'm sayin'.

JACKSON: So why are you here?

DARIUS: What?

JACKSON: You don't care what anybody thinks of you or me or your grades. So why are you outta school?

DARIUS: I'm not. I came looking for you.

JACKSON: No, you didn't.

DARIUS: Your mom sent me.

JACKSON: Why don't you call her, then? Tell her you found me.

DARIUS: I don't know her number.

JACKSON: You're here cuz you skipped outta school. What are you up to? If they sent you to mess with me, I'll scratch you.

DARIUS: Now stop it! Nobody sent me.

JACKSON: I'm callin' my mom.

DARIUS: All right, stop... Look, I accidentally — I accidentally asked out the wrong girl, okay?

JACKSON: What wrong girl?

DARIUS: Shaundra Kelly.

JACKSON: Ha! That's never gonna happen!

DARIUS: Thanks, bro.

JACKSON: So what did she say?

DARIUS: What do you think she said?

JACKSON: I think she smacked you and told you to step off.

DARIUS: She told me she'd think about it.

JACKSON: Ha! You're such an idiot! That means "no."

DARIUS: She said she'd talk to me at lunch.

JACKSON: It's almost lunchtime now. What're you doing here?

DARIUS: I'm not goin' in that cafeteria.

JACKSON: Why not?

DARIUS: Cuz you're right, all right? It's never gonna happen. And I don't need her laughin' at me in front of all her friends.

JACKSON: That would be funny.

DARIUS: Watch it.

JACKSON: You gotta eat some time, Darius.

DARIUS: I hafta cut weight for track anyway.

JACKSON: So you're afraid of a girl.

DARIUS: No, I'm not.

JACKSON: You're not in school, cuz you're afraid of a little girl.

DARIUS: You shut up. Come out of there.

(Darius tries to grab Jackson who ducks back down in the box.)

Ow! Stop scratching!

JACKSON: Stop grabbing!

(Darius glares at the box. Jackson is inside.)

So what are you gonna do? Drop out of school?

DARIUS: I wish.

JACKSON: Over Shaundra Kelly?

DARIUS: Well, I can't now.

JACKSON: Yeah, your dad'll kill you, missing class over nothing.

DARIUS: Forget that. Your mom'll kill me if she thinks I gave you the idea to do it.

(Jackson emerges again.)

JACKSON: Hey, that's right. That's exactly what she's gonna think if she finds out.

DARIUS: You better not be getting any ideas.

JACKSON: I could stay here all week and not get in trouble if she thought you put me up to it.

DARIUS: You better not.

JACKSON: Oh, man, and your dad would hear it.

DARIUS: You try it and you'll have one more person in that school that hates you.

(Jackson goes back into his box.)

Naw, come on, I'm sorry. I didn't mean it.

(After a while, Jackson sticks his head back out.)

JACKSON: You're gonna have to go back, y'know.

DARIUS: I know that.

JACKSON: Can't stay out here forever. You look like an idiot. People think you're afraid.

DARIUS: Yeah, what about you?

JACKSON: There's worse things than looking like an idiot.

DARIUS: Tell you what. Why don't we both go back?

JACKSON: What good's that gonna do?

DARIUS: Prob'ly nothing.

JACKSON: Well, then let's not. Are you crazy?

DARIUS: What if I told you from now on I'll try to have your back?

JACKSON: You think that's gonna stop 'em?

DARIUS: Maybe not. But it's something.

JACKSON: That's a terrible plan!

DARIUS: *(Giving up:)* Yeah, I guess.

JACKSON: But I guess it's worth a try.

DARIUS: Gotta start somewhere. Come on.

(Darius turns to go. Jackson stands up in his box, and eventually follows.)

You gonna lose the box?

JACKSON: Don't rush me.

DARIUS: Okay. But I'm not goin' in school with you like that.

JACKSON: We got four more blocks.

DARIUS: I'm just sayin'.

JACKSON: Don't rush me!

(Lights fade. End of play.)

The Author Speaks

What inspired you to write this play?
When I was in elementary school, I once dealt with an especially embarrassing situation by hiding in my locker for the afternoon. In hindsight, that was both terrifying and completely ridiculous.

Have you dealt with the same theme in other works that you have written?
Not the particular theme of this piece. I have dealt with dysfunctional brothers in other pieces, such as *The Stone Gift*, where these same characters exchange Christmas presents.

What writers have had the most profound effect on your style?
Douglas Adams, author of *Hitchhiker's Guide to the Galaxy*. Also Marvel comic books where I learned how to write dialogue the way real people speak.

What do you hope to achieve with this work?
The first step to solving a problem is realizing that you have a problem. The second step is realizing you need a solution. The characters in *Jax-in-a-Box* make the difficult first steps toward taking that second step.

What were the biggest challenges involved in the writing of this play?
I thought it would be fun to have a character inside a cardboard box who never comes out of it. This immediately became the biggest challenge as well, since I had to figure out how to create a scene and a relationship between two characters, one of whom might not even be "on stage" in the traditional sense.

What are the most common mistakes that occur in productions of your work?

Oftentimes, actors make the understandable mistake of "playing the comedy." That is, delivering the punch lines as if they were punch lines. Playing the scene as if they are expecting a laugh. And then being left hanging when the laugh doesn't come. Hopefully, there are plenty of funny moments in *Jax-in-a-Box*. But the "characters" are not trying to get a laugh. In fact, most of the time, Darius and Jax are kinda mad at each other. Playing the reality of the animosity between two stepbrothers is what leads to the comedy. So if an actor plays the scene as if it's a standup comedy routine, the relationship immediately becomes less believable, therefore less funny. Ironically, the harder you try to get a laugh, the less likely you'll get one.

What inspired you to become a playwright?

I've wanted to be a writer since I was a little kid. So, of course, I always assumed I was going to be a novelist. But one time, when I was in high school, I gave my creative writing teacher my new sci-fi novel that I'd been working on since junior high and he noted that the best part of my novel was the dialogue. I realized, I was spending a lot of time describing scenery and ambience that I didn't care that much about, when what I really wanted to write was funny conversations between characters. I joined the theatre department and switched over to playwriting because I realized it let me focus on my forte.

Shakespeare gave advice to the players in *Hamlet*; if you could give advice to your cast what would it be?

Have fun! Comedy is infectious. And if you're really enjoying the show, your audience will pick up on that and enjoy it as well.

About the Author

Jeff Goode is an award-winning playwright and screenwriter, the author of over 50 plays and musicals, including *THE EIGHT: Reindeer Monologues*, *Rumpelstiltskin*, *The Ubu Plays* and *Princess Gray and the Black & White Knights*. He is the creator of the Disney animated series *American Dragon: Jake Long*, and he writes for Nickelodeon's *Lalaloopsy*. Jeff is the founder of SkyPilot Theatre Company's Playwrights Wing and currently a visiting professor of playwriting for Hollins University's innovative Playwrights Lab. You can follow his misadventures on the internet at *www.jeffgoode.com*.

About YouthPLAYS

YouthPLAYS (www.youthplays.com) is a publisher of award-winning professional dramatists and talented new discoveries, each with an original theatrical voice, and all dedicated to expanding the vocabulary of theatre for young actors and audiences. On our website you'll find one-act and full-length plays and musicals for teen and pre-teen (and even college) actors, as well as duets and monologues for competition. Many of our authors' works have been widely produced at high schools and middle schools, youth theatres and other TYA companies, both amateur and professional, as well as at elementary schools, camps, churches and other institutions serving young audiences and/or actors worldwide. Most are intended for performance by young people, while some are intended for adult actors performing for young audiences.

YouthPLAYS was co-founded by professional playwrights Jonathan Dorf and Ed Shockley. It began merely as an additional outlet to market their own works, which included a substantial body of award-winning published and unpublished plays and musicals. Those interested in their published plays were directed to the respective publishers' websites, and unpublished plays were made available in electronic form. But when they saw the desperate need for material for young actors and audiences—coupled with their experience that numerous quality plays for young people weren't finding a home—they made the decision to represent the work of other playwrights as well. Dozens and dozens of authors are now members of the YouthPLAYS family, with scripts available both electronically and in traditional acting editions. We continue to grow as we look for exciting and challenging plays and musicals for young actors and audiences.

About ProduceaPlay.com

Let's put up a play! Great idea! But producing a play takes time, energy and knowledge. While finding the necessary time and energy is up to you, ProduceaPlay.com is a website designed to assist you with that third element: knowledge.

Created by YouthPLAYS' co-founders, Jonathan Dorf and Ed Shockley, ProduceaPlay.com serves as a resource for producers at all levels as it addresses the many facets of production. As Dorf and Shockley speak from their years of experience (as playwrights, producers, directors and more), they are joined by a group of award-winning theatre professionals and experienced teachers from the world of academic theatre, all making their expertise available for free in the hope of helping this and future generations of producers, whether it's at the school or university level, or in community or professional theatres.

The site is organized into a series of major topics, each of which has its own page that delves into the subject in detail, offering suggestions and links for further information. For example, Publicity covers everything from Publicizing Auditions to How to Use Social Media to Posters to whether it's worth hiring a publicist. Casting details Where to Find the Actors, How to Evaluate a Resume, Callbacks and even Dealing with Problem Actors. You'll find guidance on your Production Timeline, The Theater Space, Picking a Play, Budget, Contracts, Rehearsing the Play, The Program, House Management, Backstage, and many other important subjects.

The site is constantly under construction, so visit often for the latest insights on play producing, and let it help make your play production dreams a reality.

More from YouthPLAYS

Aesop Refabled by Nicole B. Adkins, Jeff Goode, Adam Hahn, Samantha Macher, Liz Shannon Miller, Dominic Mishler, Mike Rothschild and Dave Ulrich
Comedy. 45-60 minutes. 3-11 males, 3-11 females (3-21 performers possible).

One of L.A.'s edgiest theatre companies brings a modern spin to Aesop's classic yarns, as eight timeless fables get a 21st century reboot. Cupcake bullies, tween warriors, scheming cheerleaders and apocalyptic yellow butterfly people... Each tale takes an unexpected twist in this innovative offering!

Dear Chuck by Jonathan Dorf
Dramedy. 30-40 minutes. 8-30+ performers (gender flexible).

Teenagers are caught in the middle—they're not quite adults, but they're definitely no longer children. Through scenes and monologues, we meet an eclectic group of teens trying to communicate with that wannabe special someone, coping with a classmate's suicide, battling controlling parents, swimming for that island of calm in the stormy sea of technology—and many others. What they all have in common is the search for their "Chuck," that elusive moment of knowing who you are. Also available in a 60-70 minute version.

Sleepy Hollow by Elizabeth Doyle (music), Judy Freed (book), Owen Kalt (lyrics)
Musical Comedy. 90 minutes (may be cut down to a 60-minute version). 6+ males, 5+ females (11+ performers possible).

A scheming schoolmaster. An apprehensive heiress. A restless ghost with a penchant for decapitation. And a teenage girl who thinks demons are delightful. Nothing is as it seems in this fresh, funny adaptation of Washington Irving's classic American tale, *The Legend of Sleepy Hollow*.

The Goodcheer Home for Broken Hearts by James Grob
Comic Melodrama. 95-105 minutes. 7-30+ females, 4-30+ males (14-40+ performers possible).

Audiences get to boo, hiss, cheer and sigh in this spoof of the classic American melodrama. As the villainous Severus C. Snackwell takes aim at the Goodcheer Home for Broken Hearts, the sweet and matronly Charity Goodcheer, the smart, beautiful and great smelling Shasta Bellflower and indeed the entire backwater town of Wetwater, can the strong and sincere but soft-witted Steele Manly stop his nefarious plot?

The Grippe of October by John P. McEneny
Drama. 50-55 minutes. 13-18 females, 5-12 males (18-30 performers possible).

It starts with a cough. October 1918. Weary young soldiers return to their hometowns after the end of the fighting in Europe, bringing with them the scars of war...and a mysterious illness that spreads like wildfire. As it reaches pandemic proportions, sheltered young Alice McMahon must put aside her dreams of the stage to tend to the sick and dying, rich and poor alike, one of many lives that will be forever changed by the Spanish Flu that killed more people than the Great War it followed.

Telling William Tell by Evan Guilford-Blake
Dramedy. 80-85 minutes. 7-11 males, 4-10 females (11-21 performers possible).

The children grab the spotlight in this retelling of the story of the mythical Swiss hero—famed for shooting an apple off his son's head—framed by a fictionalized story of Rossini writing his famed opera. Music by the great composer enriches this thrilling tale of Switzerland's fight for freedom and the birth of a new work of musical art.

Made in the USA
Charleston, SC
10 October 2014